STAIRS!

Are you destined to be a maid or are you meant for better things? My fun game will reveal all!

HOW TO PLAY:

- Play with one or more friends and use pennies or buttons for counters.
- Throw a 6 on the dice to start.
- Move round the board — if you land on a picture you must follow the matching instructions for the square.
- If you land on a gemstone you can move forward 2 spaces.
- Land on the wooden spoon and you must throw a 6 to move on.
- Winner is the first person to the end — pick either the black diamond or sparkling sapphire to reveal your destiny!

4 EEK! COOK MAKES YOU CHOP UP PIG TROTTERS. DISGUSTING! GO BACK 3 SPACES.

10 YOU DROP A GLOVE AND A VERY HANDSOME GENTLEMAN RETRIEVES IT. MOVE FORWARD 2 SPACES.

15 BREAKFAST ARRIVES! UGH — IT'S WATERY GRUEL. GO BACK 1 SPACE.

22 MISS A TURN WHILE YOU DARN SOME SOCKS.

34 YOU BECOME KNOWN AS THE BEST DESIGNER OF BEAUTIFULLY ELEGANT FANS. TAKE ANOTHER TURN.

43 YOU MUST SCRUB THE PRIVY FLOOR TILL IT'S SPOTLESS. GO BACK 4.

52 A SECRET ADMIRER SENDS YOU FLOWERS. MOVE FORWARD 1 SPACE.

65 OOPS! YOU BREAK A PRICELESS VASE WHILST DUSTING. GO BACK 2 SPACES.

80 QUEEN VICTORIA INVITES YOU TO TEA AT THE PALACE. HAVE ANOTHER TURN.

86 TOPPING UP THE FIRES WITH COAL TAKES AGES! GO BACK 3 SPACES.

93 SUCCESS! CHARLES DICKENS IS PUBLISHING YOUR MEMOIRS. MOVE FORWARD 4.

YOU CHOSE:

 SAPPHIRE BLUE — You will live upstairs as lady of the house.

 BLACK DIAMOND — Uh–oh! Downstairs maid for you, we're afraid!

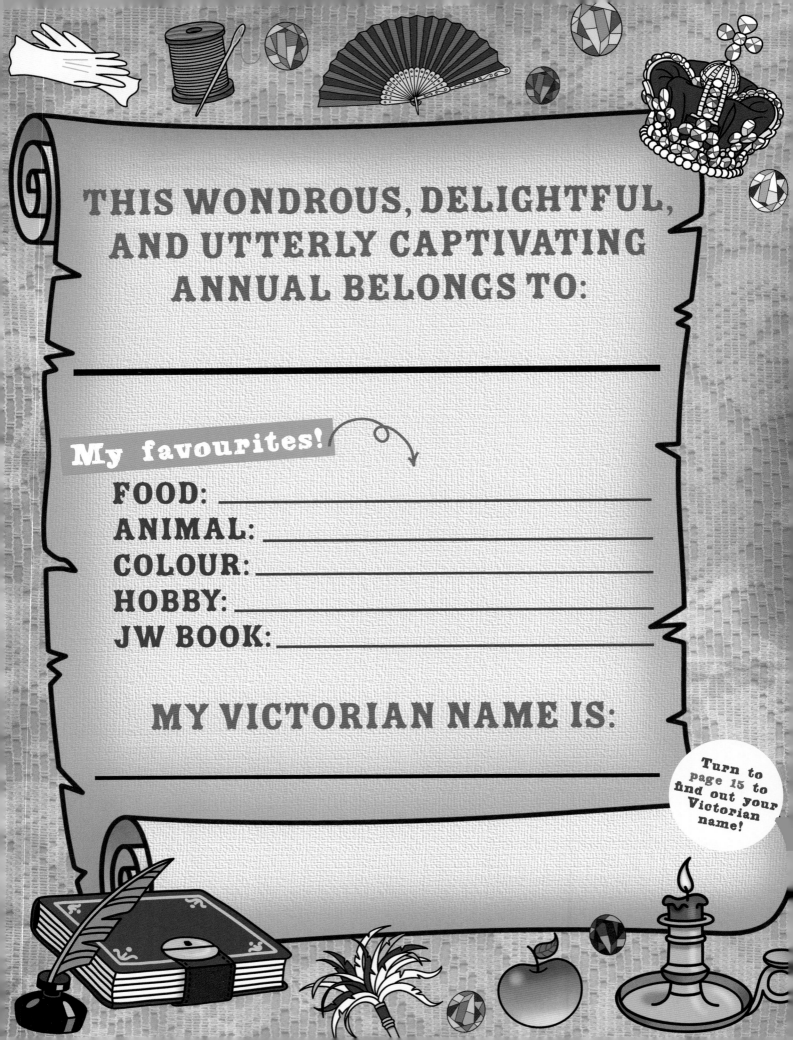

THIS WONDROUS, DELIGHTFUL, AND UTTERLY CAPTIVATING ANNUAL BELONGS TO:

_____

My favourites!

FOOD: _____
ANIMAL: _____
COLOUR: _____
HOBBY: _____
JW BOOK: _____

MY VICTORIAN NAME IS:

_____

Turn to page 15 to find out your Victorian name!

HETTY FEATHER

FEISTY AND FUNNY

In 1876 a tiny blue—eyed baby with fiery red hair is left at The Foundling Hospital and Hetty's story begins...

STARRING...

JEM

GIDEON AND SAUL

MADAME ADELINE

IDA

ELIJAH THE PERFORMING ELEPHANT

BORN: 1876
FOUNDLING NO: 25629
LIKES: Her best friend Polly, story—telling
DISLIKES: Matron Stinking Bottomly!

Turn over to enter the exciting world of Hetty Feather!

All about me, from A–Z!

A I was truly amazed when I first saw Madame Adeline perform on her horse, Pirate. She has flame–red hair, just like mine!

B Matron Stinking Bottomly once locked me away in a tiny attic room as punishment.

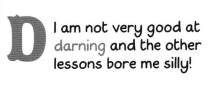

D I am not very good at darning and the other lessons bore me silly!

E Little Eliza is another of Mother's foster babies.

C Jem and I snuck off to see Mr Tanglefield's Circus. It was one of the best days of my life!

F Mothers give their babies to the Foundling Hospital when they cannot look after them. I am one of those unfortunate babies, now known as a 'foundling'.

G I am very protective of Gideon, my foster brother. He too was abandoned as baby.

H How I hate my foundling name, Hetty! I fancy my birth mother would have called me Sapphire.

I Dear Ida is the loveliest, most generous maid in the hospital. She is almost like a mother to me.

J One day my foster brother, Jem, will come for me and we shall be married. We aren't actually related, of course!

K We girl foundlings are expected to find a position as a kitchen maid when we leave the hospital at age 14.

L I stitched lavender hearts to give to Ida and my friends for Christmas.

HETTY FEATHER

M How I loved my foster mother, Peg! Gideon and I cried sorely when we were parted from her.

N My foundling number is 25629.

O Every Christmas at the hospital is the same — we all receive an orange and a new penny.

P Polly is my dear foundling friend. She is such a sweet girl.

Q We were all so excited to attend Queen Victoria's Golden Jubilee celebrations.

R Matron Pigface took my beloved rag baby! I shall never forgive her.

S I treasure the silver sixpence Jem gave to me as a parting gift

T The matrons say I have a wicked temper because of my fiery red hair!

U The foundling uniform is so coarse, drab and ugly. One day I will wear a glorious dress of emerald green.

V When I ran away from the hospital, I teamed up with a friendly street vagrant named Sissy.

W I do so love Nurse Winnie. Aside from Ida, she is the only nice person who looks after us here at the hospital.

X Ida often sneaks me an extra potato or a sprinkling of sugar when she serves me dinner!

Y I was born in the year 1876.

Z I have a particular zeal for writing — one day I hope to be a writer, just like my friend, Miss Smith!

HETTY FEATHER'S FOUNDLING

DISCOVER WHAT IT WAS LIKE TO LIVE AT THE FOUNDLING HOSPITAL!

This is the Foundling Hospital! It looks a little different today and inside you'll find the Foundling Museum where you can learn about its history.

THE FOUNDLING HOSPITAL WAS SET UP BY THOMAS CORAM IN 1741. HE WAS APPALLED BY THE NUMBER OF ABANDONED AND HOMELESS CHILDREN ON THE STREETS OF LONDON SO HE DECIDED TO GIVE THEM SOMEWHERE TO LIVE, WORK AND EAT.

Babies who were left at the Foundling Hospital were given a number and a new name. In *Hetty Feather*, Gideon's number is 25621.

What would your number and new name be?

My number was 25629.

My Foundling name:

....

My Foundling number:

....

Foundlings had to wear starched dresses and pinafores made out of a scratchy fabric called serge, and boots that often didn't fit.

JW fan Lucie Davis visited the Foundling Museum!

Traditional Foundling uniform.

LIFE!

Food was plain and simple. Bread was made in the kitchen, although it wasn't the delicious soft white loaf you'd recognise today.

There were wonderful works of art on display in the Foundling Hospital. Famous artists such as William Hogarth and Richard Wilson donated their paintings and rich men and women would go to see them. The paintings are still on display today!

Boys and girls were separated at the hospital. They weren't allowed to talk or play with each other and only saw each other from a distance.

Lucie sits in front of the famous Foundling paintings!

DID YOU KNOW?

THE FIRST TWO FOUNDLINGS WERE CALLED THOMAS CORAM AND EUNICE CORAM AFTER THE FOUNDER AND HIS WIFE!

At the age of six, girls took on housekeeping duties in order to make them more appealing to future employers. Boys were educated until the age of twelve when they were sent out into the world to work.

Tokens were left as 'identifiers' by mothers when they left their babies at the hospital. They were to help mothers find their child, should they ever return to claim them.

Foundlings were encouraged to play outside and boys played with bats, balls and javelin!

Turn to page 10 to find out more about identifiers!

FIND OUT MORE AT WWW.FOUNDLINGMUSEUM.ORG.UK

CREATE AN IDENTIFIER!

Imagine you're a Foundling and design your own token!

Identifiers or 'tokens' were often left by mothers when they gave their babies to the Foundling Hospital in the hope that they could be reunited later. Think about how your Foundling identifier might look.

Two of the identifiers on display at the Foundling Museum!

DRAW YOUR IDENTIFIER HERE –

Perhaps your identifier is a lock with your family emblem on it.

How about a special friendship bracelet that connects you to your mum?

What material will your token be made from? Many Victorians used scraps of fabric, small metal disks or inexpensive jewellery.

Think about which colours were used in Victorian times. It's unlikely you'd find neon pink as Victorians favoured luxurious shades such as bronze red, forest green and rich brown.

What do you think your birth parents would write on your identifier? Perhaps it's just their initials, or maybe they'd write a touching message for you to read when you're older.

ARE YOU A HOT CROSS HETTY?

Take the tick test to find out!

YOUR BF TURNS UP TO YOUR PARTY AN HOUR LATE! YOU...

- ☐ Refuse to let her in. You can't abide lateness! **3 points**
- ☐ Grab her in a bear-hug and tell her how glad you are to see her. **1 point**
- ☐ Welcome her inside, but not before frowning pointedly at your watch. **2 points**

WHO DID YOU LAST FALL OUT WITH?

- ☐ No-one. You can't stand arguments. **1 point**
- ☐ Your BF — you bicker a LOT! **3 points**
- ☐ Your annoying sibling. **2 points**

DAD ASKS YOU TO HELP HIM CLEAN THE CAR. YOU...

- ☐ Get stuck in — the sooner it's done, the sooner you can start reading *JW Mag*. **1 point**
- ☐ 'Disappear' off upstairs in a boiling rage. It's not your turn! **3 points**
- ☐ Mutter 'why me?' under your breath while you scrub the wheels. **2 points**

THE CAT KNOCKS OVER THE CLAY MODEL YOU SPENT HOURS MAKING, SMASHING IT. YOU...

- ☐ Shake your fist at the cat and chuck the pieces in the bin. **3 points**
- ☐ Fix it with a bit of glue and carefully paint over the cracks. **2 points**
- ☐ Start all over again and vow to put it in a safe place this time. **1 point**

PICK YOUR ULTIMATE PET HATE!

- ☐ L-o-n-g queues! You wait for no-one. **3 points**
- ☐ Untidiness. There's just no need for mess. **2 points**
- ☐ People with bad manners. It's just plain rude. **1 point**

YOUR PESKY BROTHER SPILLS PAINT ALL OVER YOUR FAVE JUMPER. YOU...

- ☐ Wonder what you can wear instead. **1 point**
- ☐ Pull a sad face and secretly hope Mum might buy you a replacement! **2 points**
- ☐ Clasp the ruined jumper to your chest and wail for hours. **3 points**

NOW ADD UP YOUR POINTS!

1-6 POINTS
CALM & COLLECTED
Hetty could do with a pinch of your patience! You're level-headed and sensible, no matter what — you're definitely not one to make a fuss!

7-12 POINTS
QUITE CRANKY!
It can take a lot to get you flustered, but when you do, you can get pretty cross. Try to remain calm and look at the situation again. You'll soon find a solution.

13-18 POINTS
TEMPER TANTRUM!
Your dramatic and flamboyant personality means you often explode in stressful situations! Try counting to ten before you react and breathe slowly and deeply.

A FOUNDLING

Play along to create your very own Foundling Hospital story!

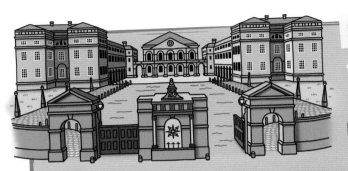

START HERE!

1. Where in the Foundling Hospital will your tale take place? Choose your favourite colour to pick a location!

THE GREAT DINING HALL AT DINNER TIME.

IN MATRON BOTTOMLY'S OFFICE!

MISS MORLEY'S CLASSROOM.

IN THE GIRLS' DORMITORY.

IDA'S CRAMPED BEDROOM IN THE SERVANTS' QUARTERS.

LOCKED UP IN THE ATTIC ROOM!

2. Roll a dice to find your main character!

1. HETTY FEATHER
2. SWEET POLLY
3. GIDEON
4. NURSE WINNIE
5. IDA BATTERSEA
6. LITTLE ELIZA

3. Choose a card to pick an enemy!

MATRON PIGFACE!

MATRON BOTTOMLY

MISS MORLEY

SHEILA

TALE...

4. Add up the numbers in your date of birth to pick a plot for your story!

FOR EXAMPLE:
18.10.2003 = 1 + 8 + 1 + 0 + 2 + 0 + 0 + 3 = 15
Keep adding until you get 9 or less: 1 + 5 = 6

1. One Foundling child will be adopted by a kind, wealthy couple. But who will it be?

2. A cooked ham mysteriously disappears from Cook's kitchen! Who is the culprit?

3. A very important visitor arrives with unexpected news...

4. Two Foundlings escape and run away! Who are they, and where are they going?

5. There is a terrible fire in the kitchen. Will everyone survive?

6. A new matron makes the children's lives an absolute misery...

7. Someone discovers a secret stash of money in a long—forgotten, dusty room!

8. There is an outbreak of influenza and many children fall ill...

9. A stray cat wanders into the dormitory! Can the girls hide it from Matron?

Now write your story! Don't forget to include lots of descriptive words and exciting plot twists to bring your tale to life!

FRIENDS OR FOES?

How many of my friends (or foes!) can you name?

Hint: She means the world to me.

Hint: I cried when she locked me away in the attic room.

Hint: A true lady and a great friend!

Hint: He taught me how to read.

VICTORIOUS VICTORIA!

Find out about the queen who reigned during my life!

QUEEN VICTORIA WAS BORN ALMOST 200 YEARS AGO — ON 24TH MAY 1819.

QUEEN VICTORIA

In 1837, after her uncle died, Victoria became Queen aged just 18 years old!

DID YOU KNOW?

Victoria is Queen Elizabeth II's great-great grandmother!

THREE YEARS LATER, IN 1840, SHE MARRIED HER HUSBAND, PRINCE ALBERT — THEY HAD NINE CHILDREN TOGETHER.

PRINCE ALBERT

DID YOU KNOW?

Victoria was a talented artist and loved painting and drawing.

When Albert died in 1861, Victoria was very sad. At the time, people mourning the loss of a loved one were expected to wear black for a year, but because Victoria was so upset, she decided to wear black for the rest of her life!

VICTORIA DIED ON 22ND JANUARY 1901 AT OSBORNE HOUSE, WHICH WAS HER BELOVED HOME ON THE ISLE OF WIGHT. FROM START TO FINISH, HER REIGN LASTED AN ASTONISHING 64 YEARS!

FIND YOUR VICTORIAN NAME!

To find your first name, just use your birth date — your surname is the month you were born in.

FIRST NAME

1. FLORENCE
2. ETHEL
3. BERTHA
4. MINNIE
5. BESSIE
6. GERTRUDE
7. MARTHA
8. MILDRED
9. JOSEPHINE
10. VIOLA
11. EFFIE
12. MARGUERITE
13. OLIVE
14. LUCILLE
15. HENRIETTA
16. MAUD
17. LEONORA
18. GENEVIEVE
19. IRMA
20. WINIFRED
21. LUELLA
22. TILLIE
23. OPAL
24. GUSSIE
25. BONNIE
26. ZELLA
27. LUCINDA
28. ALVINA
29. EUGENIA
30. OPHELIA
31. MINERVA

DID YOU KNOW?

Victoria kept a diary and wrote in it regularly.

SURNAME

JANUARY: Alardice
FEBRUARY: Barnbary
MARCH: Tanner
APRIL: Spice
MAY: Uleaven
JUNE: Vabsley
JULY: Jewkes
AUGUST: Crumb
SEPTEMBER: Pawkins
OCTOBER: Snagsby
NOVEMBER: Applebee
DECEMBER: Nankervis

My Victorian name is Leonora Nankervis!

Don't forget to fill in page four and include your Victorian name!

My Victorian name is:

Irma Nankervis

15

YOUR VICTORIAN

Discover your Victorian destiny!

MAID

You're hard working, sensible and get things done without a fuss. Perhaps you'd be a scullery maid and keep the kitchen clean or a chamber maid who makes sure the bedrooms are always neat and tidy.

TEACHER

To you, there's nothing better than reading and learning something new. That's why you'd make a fantastic teacher! You'd write on a blackboard with chalk, use an abacus to teach maths and make sure every pupil's handwriting was neat.

TAILOR

You've got a great sense of style and you're well organised, which would make you a fabulous tailor! Maybe you'd make a morning suit for a wealthy gentleman or sew an intricate silk dress for an aristocratic lady!

START

You make new friends easily.

You give your BF great advice. — NO

YES — Your chores are always done. — NO

YES → MAID

NO

Art is your favourite subject.

YES

YES → Always got your head in a book? — YES → TEACHER

NO

You're neat and tidy.

YES

NO

You like to customise your clothes. — YES → TAILOR

NO

You're quite messy.

YES

NO

Always run out of pocket money?

16

LIFE

You love shopping. → YES → **Confident & outgoing — that's you!**

NO

YES

You're super organised.

NO

YES → **Confident & outgoing — that's you!** → YES

NO

You prefer working in a team. → YES

You'd love to be rich & famous.

NO

NO

YES

YES → **You like going out for dinner.** → YES

NO

SHOP KEEPER

Your friendly manner and organisational skills would make you a top shop keeper! Perhaps you'd sell delicious treats in a sweet shop or bakery. Yum! Or how about a toy shop where you could play with puppets and porcelain dolls?

FACTORY WORKER

You're enthusiastic and like spending time with your friends. That would make you an excellent factory worker! You might work in a jute mill weaving fabric or maybe in a printing factory putting together wonderful Victorian books!

VICTORIAN LADY

You'd make the ideal Victorian lady! Imagine being dressed in fine satin and silk and feasting on enormous banquets. You'd also get taken everywhere in a horse and carriage. How sophisticated!

ODD JOBS!

Have you heard of these unusual Victorian jobs?

MARSHALL
A horse doctor who fitted horses with new shoes!

WAINWRIGHT
A builder or repairer of wagons.

KNOCKER-UP
Someone who knocked on windows to make sure people weren't late for work.

BLACK BORDERER
Someone who made black-edged stationery for funerals.

READ MORE ABOUT VICTORIAN FUNERAL CUSTOMS ON PAGE 54!

VICTORIAN FASHION DESIGNER

Learn all about Victorian dresses and design a gown for Hetty!

LUXURIOUS FABRICS

Victorian ladies wore highly decorative gowns of rich, sumptuous fabrics that fitted beautifully and swished as they walked. Remember when Hetty fashioned herself a 'Sunday best' dress from green velvet and gold curtain cord.

What kind of fabric do you think Hetty would choose for her dress if money was of no object? How about a crinkly taffeta or smooth silk? Perhaps she'd stick to soft velvet, but in a different colour... The choice is yours!

TRIMS & RUFFLES

The Victorians definitely didn't believe in the saying, 'Less is more'! They loved to go over–the–top with everything, from decorating their homes to dressing themselves up. Dressmakers finished their creations with ruffles, layers of silk, buttons and lace collars.

Stick on sweet wrappers for fantastic coloured ruffles or paper doilies to look like lace. You could also use small buttons or braided thread for finishing touches.

DAINTY HANDS & FEET

Every upper–class Victorian lady wore gloves. They had shoes and boots made from expensive soft leather or suede. Many styles were trimmed with a row of gold or silver buttons, with a little heel and a pointed toe.

Do you think Hetty would be able to walk in a heel? After all, she's used to wearing the clumpy foundling boots! Have a think, and design a gorgeous pair of shoes for her!

ELEGANT EMBROIDERY

Hetty is a dab hand with a needle and thread — she can embroider beautifully decorated initials and patterns on just about anything! The Victorians loved natural patterns, like trailing flowers, insects or birds.

Try drawing simple designs on a scrap of paper and choose which you like best before adding it to your gown. An embroidered bodice looks lovely — or how about a floral hem?

GLITZ & JEWELS

Accessorise Hetty's beautiful new gown with delicate antique jewellery. The Victorians were also very fond of cameo jewellery — this is a pendant or brooch showing the silhouette of a loved one. Perhaps Hetty would have a cameo of her dear mama pinned to her bodice, or hung on a gold chain round her neck.

Victorian jewellery is very ornate — look up 'Victorian jewellery' on the internet for design inspiration!

Use colouring pencils, pens, paint or even scraps of fabric to create a unique gown!

SAY IT WITH *flowers!*

Find out more about this fun way Victorians communicated!

Forget texting, emailing and instant messenger — way back in the Victorian era, communication was a lot more... flowery!

That's because the Victorians believed that flowers symbolised certain emotions and could be used to send secret messages. This method of sending messages was called floriography. A floriographer (someone who sent flower messages) believed that by sending a specific flower type or colour, the recipient would know what it meant!

THE FLOWER OF LOVE!

One of the most common messages signified by flowers was that the sender loved the recipient — all these flowers were known to represent love...

FORGET-ME-NOT

HONEYSUCKLE

TULIPS

MYRTLE

LILAC

PRIMROSE

Did you know?

When Kate Middleton married Prince William, her bouquet contained a sprig of myrtle that came from a plant that had originally been in one of Queen Victoria's bouquets!

COOL CARNATIONS!

Carnations were a popular choice for floriographers — but certain colours meant different things!

RED = yes

YELLOW = no

MULTI-COLOURED = maybe

PINK = I'll never forget you

WEIRD & WONDERFUL!

Aside from love and romance, flowers could also signify some rather unusual emotions...

FOXGLOVE = a wish

JASMINE = you are cheerful and graceful

SWEET PEA = pride and appreciation

SNOWDROP = consolation or hope

GUESS WHO!

Can you think of a JW book where I use the flower marigold to symbolise despair? Clue: it's the name of one of my acharacters!

THE REAL MISS SMITH

Miss Smith helps Hetty and Sissy and becomes a great friend, but did you know she was also a real–life inspiring author?

Sarah Smith was born in 1832. Her dad owned a book shop and Sarah loved reading the books there. Soon she began writing her own stories, but for years none of them were published.

Then her sister Elizabeth secretly sent one of the stories to Charles Dickens. He decided to print it in his magazine *Household Words* and paid Sarah £5. That's worth around £360 in today's money!

Soon Sarah was regularly writing for the magazine and she and Charles became fast friends.

The Smith family had a strict religious life, so Sarah's stories were very moral and encouraged people to do good. She often wrote about the hard lives of homeless and orphaned children — just like Hetty and Sissy!

In 1858 Sarah started to write under her new author name of Hesba Stretton. The Victorians loved her tales of despair with dramatic titles such as *Alone in London* and *Highway of Sorrow*.

In the 1800s women were often considered silly and unimportant, but Sarah was good at business. She insisted she was fairly paid and, because she wasn't married, was able to sign her own book contracts. A married lady would have to ask her husband's permission!

Sarah's most famous and best–loved book was *Jessica's First Prayer*, which was a massive success. By the end of the 1800s it had sold over one and a half million copies — 10 times more than the very famous *Alice in Wonderland*! Sarah kept writing and used her fame to help children living in the terrible Victorian slums. She helped set up a charity that would later become the NSPCC that we know today.

Sarah lived with Elizabeth and together they ran a book club to encourage people to learn to read. By the time she died in 1911 she had published over 40 books and countless more stories.

WHAT HAPPENS NEXT?

Jessica's First Prayer

Jessica's mother is an actress who drinks too much and forces Jess to work as a child actress. When Jessica becomes too old to get any more acting parts, her mother cruelly beats and abandons her. Jessica is alone on the streets with no money, food or family!

A kindly chapel keeper comes to her aid and gives her shelter, but what happens next?

Can Jess find new work? Will she ever see her mother again? Maybe she meets up with Hetty Feather!

It's up to you write the next chapter in Jessica's story!

WHAT'S YOUR AUTHOR NAME?

Sarah Smith used the initials of her siblings to make up the name Hesba, and Stretton came from a place she liked to visit.

Find your Victorian author name right here —

FIRST NAME:

Choose your favourite colour —

ELEANORA   SURAYA

ALYISS   ROSEMARY

VIOLET   JACINTHA

MIDDLE NAME:

The first letter of your own name ☐

SURNAME:

Match it to the *day* you were born —

MONDAY: Greenlees
TUESDAY: Copperfield
WEDNESDAY: Poppleton
THURSDAY: Bramley
FRIDAY: Shoesmith
SATURDAY: Wilberforce
SUNDAY: Binks

My Victorian author name is Jacintha J Greenlees!

My Victorian name is...

Violet . C
Poppleton

23

FRIPPERIES & FALDERALS!

The Victorians loved fancy things and were even fonder of using fancy words! The words listed below are all terms for ornaments, trimmings or decorations. How quickly can you find them in the word search?

Words can read forwards, backwards, up, down or diagonally. Letters can be used more than once. Tick them off as you go —

K	I	H	E	G	K	W	H	I	M	S	Y
C	C	L	L	Q	R	R	X	F	C	R	Z
A	B	A	G	A	T	E	L	L	E	C	F
R	Q	R	N	J	L	W	Q	M	W	O	N
C	D	E	A	K	R	Z	M	S	A	S	N
M	H	D	D	H	K	U	E	J	G	X	O
I	T	L	N	C	L	C	G	N	W	D	I
G	R	A	A	F	Z	Y	I	O	E	A	T
H	I	F	F	R	U	P	L	N	G	D	O
M	F	R	I	P	P	E	R	Y	K	O	N
E	L	B	U	A	B	I	B	E	L	O	T
F	E	O	R	R	J	D	G	V	I	D	A
W	D	T	U	Z	T	D	O	R	N	Y	H
F	R	F	I	H	F	U	U	W	I	G	W
B	W	Y	U	V	U	C	X	A	Y	H	G

- ☑ BAGATELLE
- ☑ BAUBLE
- ☐ BIBELOT
- ☐ CURIO
- ☐ DOODAD
- ☐ FALDERAL
- ☐ FANDANGLE
- ☐ FLUMMERY
- ☐ FRIPPERY
- ☐ FURBELOW
- ☐ GEWGAW
- ☐ GIMCRACK
- ☐ KNICK-KNACK
- ☐ NOTION
- ☐ TRAPPINGS
- ☐ TRIFLE
- ☐ WHATNOT
- ☐ WHIMSY

24

SAPPHIRE BATTERSEA

Formerly known as **Hetty Feather**, Sapphire Battersea leaves the safety of The Foundling Hospital and ventures into the real world. Marvel at her tale of family and friendship, first love and loss...

My name is Sapphire Battersea. Doesn't that sound beautiful? Not like that hateful Foundling label, Hetty Feather! It's ridiculous — not even like a real name! Thank goodness I'm free of that horrible place at last.

I'm now in gainful employ as maid of all works for Mr Buchanan. He is rather a strange one, with his tiny spectacles and funny little fez hat. I fancy he looks rather like an organ grinder's monkey...

TURN THE PAGE AND REVEAL MORE OF SAPPHIRE'S ADVENTURES...

Mr Clarendon's SEASIDE CURIOSITIES

Meet the amazing performers!

Do not adjust your spectacles, boys and girls — you are not seeing double! Introducing... **HAROLD, THE TWO-HEADED MARVEL!** He's a medical mystery, a biological puzzle, an enigma even the most distinguished surgeons this country has to offer cannot solve. Watch as both heads appear to smile at you and two pairs of eyes watch your every move!

Ladies and gentleman, girls and boys! Gasp in disbelief at Mr Clarendon's most popular, and 'biggest' attraction — **FANTASTIC FREDA, THE FEMALE GIANT!** Standing at over seven feet, Freda is surely taller than any man or woman who walks this earth! Clap and cheer as she strikes a pose in her magnificent bathing suit!

Roll up, roll up, come and see the new attraction at Mr Clarendon's Seaside Curiosities! Marvel at **EMERALD, THE AMAZING POCKET-SIZED MERMAID!** Sailors and suitors beware! This beautiful fish–tailed maiden with her tumbling locks of auburn hair and eyes as blue as the sea itself will steal your heart... and maybe even your soul!

Meet **HENRY, THE MAN WITH ONE HUNDRED TATTOOS!** Marvel at the intricate pictures that cover him from head to toe. See the wild creatures stampeding across his back! Count the slithering snakes that creep and wind over his torso! Laugh with delight when he flexes his muscles, making the exotic pictures dance and move!

Set sail, ye landlubbers, with **PIRATE PETE, SCOURGE OF THE SEVEN SEAS!** He's a fearsome sight with his wooden peg leg and a beard as black as coal... and just what do you think lurks behind his eye patch? You certainly wouldn't want to get too close to this scoundrel, or his bad-tempered feathered friend! Arrr!

Do you believe?

MYTHICAL MERMAIDS!

The word 'mermaid' means half woman, half fish. 'Mer' comes from the word 'sea'.

Mermaids are usually described as being very beautiful with long hair and glorious tails — just like Hetty in her costume!

The famous story of *The Little Mermaid* was written by Hans Christian Anderson in the 1800s.

Sailors have a superstition that seeing a mermaid, or hearing their voice, is bad luck.

Some people believe that mermaids can control the weather.

The Chinese believe that a mermaid's tear becomes a pearl.

LUCKY CHANCE MEMOIRS!

You can start writing your memoirs like Hetty — all you need is a dice!

Roll a dice to find out what you'll be writing about today...

1. Describe the funniest thing that happened to you today — what happened, was anyone else there and how hard did it make you laugh?

2. Did anything surprising happen to you today? Write about it! Why was it surprising and what was your reaction?

3. Write a detailed description of a person you saw today. Try to remember what they were wearing, how they spoke and if there was anything interesting or unusual about them...

4. Describe something you did today in lots of detail — as if you were explaining it to someone who had never heard of it before!

5. What was the dullest thing that happened to you today? Write about it as if it was the most exciting thing ever!

6. What did you talk about today? Write out one of your conversations as if it was a play, giving notes on the facial expressions and body language of you and the others involved.

Now roll the dice to find out which word you should write into your diary entry!

1. TREMENDOUS
2. GARGANTUAN
3. WONDERFUL
4. ATROCIOUS
5. DISGUSTING
6. MARVELLOUS

Let's add some words to describe how you felt. Roll the dice then pick which of the two words suits the tone of your diary entry best!

1. EXUBERANT **OR** DISPIRITED
2. TRIUMPHANT **OR** DEFEATED
3. FEARLESS **OR** TERRIFIED
4. UNSURPRISED **OR** FLABBERGASTED
5. EXCEPTIONAL **OR** UNREMARKABLE
6. ARRESTING **OR** TEDIOUS

Finally, fill in your very first diary entry! Here are some tips to help...

⭐ Use lots of adjectives (describing words) to give your memoirs a sense of emotion — a good way to do this is to try to describe how you felt every time you write about something you did.

⭐ Try to use interesting words — devastated is much more dramatic than sad, and it's much more exciting to say you were triumphant instead of that you won!

⭐ Write a little a lot! It can be daunting to think you have to fill a page, so set an easy target like writing three sentences a day.

BERTIE OR JEM?

★ Which of Sapphire's sweethearts do you think she should end up with?

TICK THE THINGS YOU THINK SAPPHIRE WOULD LIKE BEST. THE BOY WITH THE MOST POINTS IS THE WINNER!

FUTURE PROSPECTS

Life with Jem could mean Sapphire living in the country for the rest of her days. Would she enjoy this lifestyle?

Being with Bertie would mean Sapphire could stay in town — but would she rather escape the hustle and bustle?

KINDNESS

Jem is a good friend of Sapphire's before he becomes her sweetheart and he always looks after her best interests.

Bertie is fun and feisty and his personality is an excellent match for Sapphire.

GENEROSITY

Jem takes Sapphire to the circus — but he doesn't exactly pay for her ticket!

Bertie takes Sapphire out to the fair, on a boat ride and for a walk in the park.

AWFUL UPSET

Give the point to the boy who's upset Sapphire least!

Sapphire was upset when she discovered Jem had promised Eliza he'd marry her — even after he'd made the same promise to Sapphire! However, she later finds out he didn't mean to hurt her...

Bertie upsets Sapphire when he takes a shine to Rose-May, Mr Buchanan's new maid.

LOYALTY

Jem waits for Sapphire outside the Foundling Hospital, even though he's upset her in the past.

Bertie doesn't seem to miss Sapphire too much now that Rose-May's around!

★ YOU PICKED... ★

JEM
You're a homebody who loves to be content and comfortable... and you think Sapphire would enjoy this kind of life too! Although she's a free spirit, you think someone should keep her grounded, and the ideal person would be Jem!

BERTIE
Bertie's the boy for you! You're fun and feisty, just like the butcher's boy, and you think he would be an excellent match for Sapphire — just think of all the fun and frolics they'd have together!

Sew with Sapphire

Amaze your friends with skillful stitching — I can show you how!

Sapphire's fine sewing skills are the envy of many. Her friend, Freda, admires the pretty lazy daisies stitched on her nightgown. Follow these steps to sew your own lazy daisies...

1. Start by lightly sketching a star on your fabric as a guide — you can trace Sapphire's template. Knot the end of your thread and bring the needle through from the wrong side to the right side at the centre point.

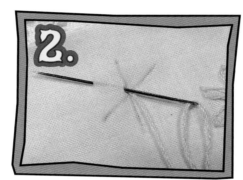

2. Start your first stitch at the base of a line. Pass the needle through the fabric to the end of the line — as if you were making a running stitch.

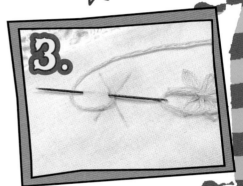

3. Wrap the thread round the front of the needle before you pull it all the way through to make a loop.

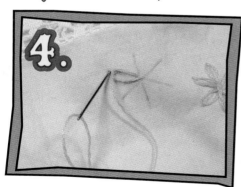

4. Now take the needle back down through the fabric just in front of the loop. The thread will form a tiny stitch to hold the petal in place — don't pull too tight.

Bring your needle back up through at the centre point again to start the next petal.

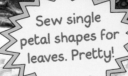

Sew single petal shapes for leaves. Pretty!

MY FAVOURITE THINGS!

Take a peep into the past with Jacky's special Victorian treasures!

These wonderful decorated teapots were used on barges in Victorian times. I've never actually made tea in mine — I just keep it on the mantlepiece.

Me wearing a very special Victorian citrine brooch.

I never tire of looking at this curious fairy painting by Richard Dadd.

Here's my beautiful Victorian doll Bluebell. Tracy Beaker's doll has the same name!

This is a comical Victorian Fairing — they were prizes at fairs. I wish you could still win them now!

Three o'clock in the morning

My daughter Emma loved to dress up in this child's Victorian dress and Red Riding Hood cape when she was little.

These are my two favourite Victorian children's books, *Little Women* and *What Katy Did*.

Which of these beautiful objects would you most like to have?

Do you have any special Victorian treasures of your own?

I love my Victorian necklace made out of Whitby jet. Can you see whose portrait I have in the locket?

DINE LIKE A

Times were hard for most Victorians and food was hard to come by. The very poorest barely survived on potato peelings, rotting veg and any scraps they could get their hands on. Starvation forced the most desperate into the workhouse — a terribly grim place where the people were forced to work very long hours in awful conditions in return for a little food and shelter.

Most Victorians ate a poor diet.

THE WORKHOUSE CAFF

TODAY'S SPECIALS:

STARTER

Bowl of gruel

(A very watery porridge with little taste — and even less vitamins!)

SIDES

A hunk of bread served with a smear of dripping and a spot of mould

MAIN

Potatoes and a chunk of cheese

Imagine eating the same thing, day in, day out!

VICTORIAN!

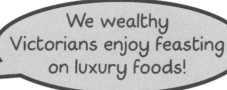

We wealthy Victorians enjoy feasting on luxury foods!

However, if you were rich you ate very well indeed! The aristocrats enjoyed showing off their wealth by throwing elaborate banquets with many, many courses served on fine china.

You are cordially invited to dine with Lady and Lord Chessington.

Dinner Menu:

First course
Vermicelli soup

Second course
Baked salmon

Third course
Lobster

Fourth course
Oysters

Fifth course
Cold meats

Entrée
**Venison
Braised beef
Potatoes, carrots and a rich gravy**

Dessert
Imported strawberries and cherries Neapolitan cakes, soufflé and éclairs.

AFTERNOON TEA

The great British tradition!

Victorian ladies enjoyed meeting up with their friends for a spot of afternoon tea. This tradition was started by Anna, the 7th Duchess of Bedford...

One late afternoon, Anna was feeling very peckish. She asked to be served a pot of tea and a snack in her bedroom. She decided to eat like this every day and began to invite her friends round to join her. Before long, it was extremely fashionable for ladies to sip tea and snack on sandwiches and cakes in the afternoon.

Oooh, I feel a bit peckish!

TEA FOR TWO
(or three, four, five!)

Why not hold your very own afternoon tea party? You can make up dainty sandwiches (without the crusts, of course!) and set the table with pretty china and delicate doilies. Ask your guests (your BFs!) to bring along a tasty cake or biscuits for everyone to enjoy.

TURN OVER TO FIND OUT HOW TO MAKE MRS B'S TEACUP CUPCAKES!

Mrs B's TEACUP CUPCAKES

SO VERY ELEGANT FOR A VICTORIAN AFTERNOON TEA!

You'll need:
- ⭐ 110g/4oz softened butter
- ⭐ 110g/4oz caster sugar
- ⭐ 2 eggs, lightly beaten
- ⭐ 110g/4oz self–raising flour
- ⭐ 1 tsp vanilla extract

Makes 12 cakes

1. Ask an adult to pre–heat the oven to 180°C/350°F/Gas mark 4. Pop 12 paper cake cases into a cake tray.

2. Cream together the caster sugar with the softened butter and stir in the beaten eggs.

3. Sift the flour into the bowl then use a large spoon to fold it into the mixture. Add vanilla extract.

4. Carefully divide the mixture between the paper cases and bake in the oven for 10–12 minutes or until golden brown and springy to touch.

Makes a cute birthday cupcake — just add a candle!

For the buttercream icing:

1. Beat 140g of softened butter with 140g of icing sugar.
2. Add another 140g of icing sugar and 1–2 tbsp of milk and beat the mixture until smooth.
3. Pipe the buttercream icing on top of each cake and add pretty pink sprinkles.
4. Pop each cupcake inside a cute teacup and serve with a lovely pot of tea... mmm!

Mrs B's MEMORY GAME

Play a traditional Victorian parlour game with your friends!

HOW TO PLAY:

- Give every player a pencil and paper.
- Start the clock! Everyone has 30 seconds to look at this page — you must try to memorise the 12 objects.
- Stop the clock! Cover the page and jot down as many items as you can remember. The player with the most correct answers wins!

CROWN

LETTER

CANDLE

PEN

BRUSH

DUSTER

BRACELET

FAN

SCONE

SPOON

FEZ

APPLE

☆ HOW DID YOU DO? ☆

1-4 CORRECT
Oh dear! Which items did you forget? Practice reciting and learning poems and songs till you know them off by heart — it's a great way to boost your memory!

5-8 CORRECT
Not bad, but you could definitely do with a little mental work-out... Try the game again, but on your own this time. Did you do any better second time round?

9-12 CORRECT
Wow! You really do have an eye for detail! Put your memory skills to good use when you study for your next school test — that A+ will be in the bag!

SAPPHIRE'S SECRET WISHES!

Turn Sapphire's dreams into reality with this story starter game!

WHAT TO DO:

Throw a dice to decide what has happened to Sapphire — then write about her amazing new life!

INSTEAD OF HER PLAIN SERVANT'S ROBES, SAPPHIRE NOW WEARS...

1. A sparkly shawl dotted with sequins.
2. A yellow satin dress with big puffy sleeves.
3. A gold ring set with glittering diamonds.
4. A purple velvet coat with gold tassels.
5. An elegant hat with a big red ribbon.
6. A silver locket with a secret photo inside it.

INSTEAD OF SLEEPING IN THE TINY SCULLERY, SAPPHIRE NOW LIVES IN...

1. A giant castle complete with turrets.
2. A pretty cottage with a crackling open fire.
3. A manor house with a luxurious four-poster bed.
4. A cosy flat above a Victorian cake shop!
5. The house she used to serve in. Now *she's* the Lady!
6. A cabin on a boat sailing around the continent!

INSTEAD OF WORKING ALL DAY, SAPPHIRE NOW...

1. Tries on expensive clothes in Victorian dress shops.
2. Dines out on afternoon tea and delicious cakes.
3. Goes galloping over the hills on her dashing black horse.
4. Takes long walks in the beautiful countryside.
5. Spends her time in an attic room writing her memoirs.
6. Becomes idle and bored and wishes for her old life back.

WHAT ARE SAPPHIRE'S FAVOURITE THINGS TO EAT NOW?

1. Afternoon tea with big slabs of walnut cake — yummy!

2. Everything! She enjoys six course meals on a daily basis.

3. Seafood dishes like lobster, oysters, and caviar. Very posh!

4. She's got a taste for lamb tongue, actually.

5. An endless supply of luxury cheeses and bread.

6. A big roast dinner with at least two vegetable side dishes.

EVERY MORNING SAPPHIRE...

1. Sprays herself with lovely smelling scents.

2. Powders her face.

3. Puts on a pair of sparkly, dangly earrings.

4. Gets her maid to style her hair for her.

5. Takes two hours to decide on a luxury dress to wear.

6. Wears gorgeous silk gloves that go up to her elbows!

Write about Sapphire's new life here! You might also want to include how all of this happened to her, and if she's happier now — or not!

Madame Berenice's MYSTIC BALL!

I can read your future!

You can ask the mystic ball anything! Why not ask a question about friendship, family or school?

What would you ask in Victorian times?

Concentrate on the mystic ball to get a truly accurate fortune!

Try it out with your BF!

A big change will bring happiness to your life.

It's not the right time for you. Ask again later.

A special friend holds an important secret that will help you.

It's right around the corner. Think positively!

Good fortune will be yours if you smile at the next person you see.

Only *you* can answer the question. Look into your heart...

PAST LIVES!

Tick the statements you agree with and find your Victorian life!

- ☐ **I'M WELL BEHAVED.**
- ☐ **I'M CREATIVE.**
- ☐ **I LIKE BAKING.**
- ☐ **I ♥ THE OUTDOORS.**
- ☐ **I SLEEP A LOT.**
- ☐ **I CAN BE LOUD.**

★ ★ ★

MAINLY PINK
You're polite and enjoy relaxing. Being a lady of the house would be your dream Victorian life!

MAINLY BLUE
You're smart and imaginative. Life as a street urchin would be no problem for you!

EQUAL PINK/BLUE
You've got lots of hobbies and you make friends easily. Why not become a Victorian mystical spiritualist?

TINY HAT HAIR SLIDES

Decorate your hair with Victorian-inspired accessories.

A great way to use all your craft scraps!

YOU'LL NEED:

- Plastic bottle caps
- Card
- Glue
- Nail polish or acrylic paint
- Scraps of fabric, felt, ribbon, lace, net and feathers
- Stick-on sparkles
- Hair slides or a hairband

1 For each tiny hat, paint a bottle cap with nail polish then set aside to dry. To make a hat brim, cut a circle of card slightly larger than your bottle top.

2 Cover each side of the circle with fabric or felt, or paint it with nail polish.

③ Next it's time to add all your hat trimmings!

Glue on a little strip of ribbon and then you can go wild with bows, flowers, feathers and sparkles — remember the Victorians loved lots of embellishments!

④ Glue the top to the hat brim then let everything dry completely.

⑤ When you've finished decorating, glue or tape a hair grip or slide to the back. Leave to dry completely before wearing.

WHY NOT?

STICK A TINY HAT TO A HAIRBAND OR ATTACH A PIN TO THE BACK TO MAKE A BROOCH.

I look gorgeous pinned to a bun!

43

How To Draw
MERMAID EMERALD!
Nick shows you how!

1. Draw Emerald's chin first — it's a wide V shape with a little ear on one side. For her hair, draw a long, slightly squiggly line from the bottom of her chin, round her head and along where her back will be. Add in Emerald's neck and arm, and the front of her bodice.

2. Now draw Emerald's other arm and add a bracelet at the end. Continue drawing her body by sketching sweeping curved lines for her back and tail.

3. Add in Emerald's hands, then start drawing her hair. Fill in the strands of hair on the left of her head first, then move to her fringe, finishing with the long, flowing locks at the back of her head. Don't forget to add in the frilly detailing on her bodice and the end of her tail.

4. Now draw Emerald's face and the rest of the details on her costume. She has spots on her bodice and scales on her tail. She's also wearing a pretty shell necklace. Once you've drawn all these, it's time to colour her in!

Nick's Tip!

Take your time over the detailing like Emerald's hair and her tail — it's tricky to do, but worth it!

EMERALD STAR

The life of Hetty Feather has been full of drama, danger and heartbreak. Now ready to face a brave new adventure, she is Emerald Star. Which path will she choose? Will it lead to happiness?

My dear mama has instructed me to look for my father so I must travel north. It's a long journey for one to undertake alone and who knows what I might find at the end.

But I, the amazing Emerald Star, shall step forward unafraid. Nothing can stand in the way of my true destiny...

★ ★ ★

WHAT WILL EMERALD'S FUTURE HOLD? TURN THE PAGE TO FIND OUT MORE...

HAPPY EVER AFTER?

Let your imagination run wild and write a brand new Emerald Star story!

EMERALD STAR HAS THREE PATHS TO CHOOSE FROM —
HER LONG-LOST FATHER, HER BELOVED JEM OR A MYSTERIOUS
FIGURE FROM HER PAST. WRITE A BRAND NEW ENDING FOR EACH
THEN PICK THE PATH YOU THINK SHE SHOULD TAKE!

☆ PATH 1

Emerald finally meets her long—lost father. However, when she
receives a letter from Jem, she decides to leave...
Write a new ending here —

....

....

....

- What if Emerald had never found her father?
- Perhaps Emerald could begin her own life!
- Should she stay with her true family?

☆ PATH 3

Tanglefield's Circus arrives in town
and Emerald is reunited with Madame
Adeline and Diamond. When the
circus leaves, so does Emerald...
Write an alternative ending!

....

....

....

☆ PATH 2

Reunited with her beloved Jem,
Emerald looks after the family
when tragedy strikes. But a love
triangle and Tanglefield's Circus
force her to move on...
Write a new ending here —

....

....

....

- What if Jem proposed to Emerald?
- What would make Emerald stay in Carter's Bray?
- Perhaps Diamond needs her more than Jem does.

- Perhaps Emerald stays with Jem.
- Maybe Jem falls in love with another.
- Will Emerald return to Carter's Bray in the future?

EMERALD SHOULD PICK PATH NUMBER ....
BECAUSE ....

Come on a family journey with me!

FAMILY TRAIL!

Sapphire has just discovered the true identity of her mum. Imagine how it must have felt to find out where she really came from! Here are some questions to ask your parents to find out more about your own family...

WHEN AND WHERE WERE YOU BORN?

Mum: ....

....

Dad: ....

WHERE DID YOU LIVE WHEN YOU WERE GROWING UP?

Mum: ....

Dad: ....

WHICH FAMILY MEMBER ARE YOU MOST LIKE?

Mum: ....

Dad: ....

DID YOU HAVE ANY PETS?

Mum: ....

Dad: ....

WHO IS THE OLDEST RELATIVE YOU CAN REMEMBER?

Mum: ....

Dad: ....

HAVE ANY STORIES, RECIPES OR HEIRLOOMS BEEN PASSED DOWN THE FAMILY?

Mum: ....

....

Dad: ....

....

DESCRIBE YOUR MUM AND DAD AND BROTHERS AND SISTERS...

Mum: ....

....

....

Dad: ....

....

....

Find out what your surname means and where it comes from!

My surname is English and means 'Son of William'!

TURN THE PAGE TO COMPLETE YOUR FAMILY TREE!

FIND YOUR FAMILY!

Who knows, maybe you're related to a Victorian maid like Hetty!

MATERNAL GREAT-GREAT-GRANDPARENTS

MATERNAL GREAT-GRAND-PARENTS

MATERNAL GRAND-PARENTS

MUM

WHY NOT?
Add photographs of your relatives to your family tree.

WHAT TO DO:

Start by writing your name in the middle, and then add in your siblings, your parents and your grandparents. How far back you go is completely up to you — if you're feeling brave, you could make a giant one and include aunts and uncles, cousins, great-grandparents and more!

FIND YOUR FAMILY!

Ask if you can speak to older relatives in your family like your grandparents or great-aunts and great-uncles. You might want to set up an interview and take notes while they talk.

SOME QUESTIONS YOU COULD ASK:

Where were you born and where did you grow up?

What were the names of your parents?

What chores did you have to do growing up?

What was my mum/dad like when they were younger?

Ask if your relatives have any documents you could look at — these could be birth certificates, old newspaper clippings, postcards, or old photographs.

DAD

PATERNAL GRAND-PARENTS

PATERNAL GREAT-GRAND-PARENTS

PATERNAL GREAT-GREAT-GRANDPARENTS

ME & MY SIBLINGS

PEN A SEASIDE POEM!

Imagine you're at the beach!

Writing a poem is just another way of telling a story in a simple or more compact way. Poems can be about any subject you like, but today we're going to write about the seaside!

First of all, you need to have a think about your subject. If you can, go to a beach near you and get inspired. It's much better to see things in real life! Don't just think about what you can see, you also want to consider what you can smell, hear, taste and even feel as well.

Here's our poem! We've rhymed the first and the third lines here.

I build a castle out of sand
Then picnic on a blanket
Everyone is brown and tanned
Laughing in the water.

I squelch on the seaweed on the shore
Then dig a hole with a bucket and spade
Now it's time to get an ice cream
Mint choc chip – it's lucky Mum's paid!

In this poem we rhymed the second and fourth lines.

In this poem, the narrator is a dog. We also haven't rhymed anything at all!

Running around with driftwood in my mouth
Sniffing at red and purple jellyfish
Diving into the cold sea
My coat wet and pink tongue panting
It's great to be a dog at the beach.

↙

....

....

....

....

....

....

BONUS ROUND

What to do:

For extra poetry points, try to include one of these words in your poem. You just have to throw a dice to work out which one!

1 JELLYFISH
2 SEASHELL
3 MERMAID
4 BEACH BALL
5 PIER
6 SANDCASTLE

TOP TIPS!

⭐ Do several different drafts of your poem. It isn't going to be perfect straight away, so keep writing and re-writing until you're happy with it.

⭐ You don't have to be **you** in your poem. You could be a dog, like in our poem, or a seagull, an elderly lady, even a sandcastle!

⭐ Pay attention to the words you're using. Instead of saying 'walk' could you say 'trudged' or 'skipped' or 'marched' — these will help to give the reader a more accurate picture in their mind.

⭐ Use comparisons when you're describing things. Maybe you could say that seashells glint in the sand like glittering diamond rings?

⭐ Don't feel pressurised to rhyme every line. It's not the most important thing, and lots of professional poets don't do it. Yes, really!

⭐ Try using lots of words of the same sound. An example could be using lots of words beginning with the letter s, such as sand, shore and seashell. This is called alliteration and is a technique that lots of poets use!

⭐ Read your poem out loud when you've finished. If a line is too long or anything sounds a bit clunky then go back and revise it.

⭕ WHAT CAN YOU SEE?

Does the sand stretch out as far as the eye can see? Or perhaps there's a pier packed full of rides, food stalls, and mysterious fortune tellers? Are you alone on a secret, hidden beach, or is it noisy and crowded?

⭕ WHAT CAN YOU SMELL?

Do you smell the salt in the air from the sea? Or are your surroundings really stinky and fishy — yuck! Maybe you can smell the waft of fish and chips and other delicious foods in the air — are they making you hungry?

⭕ WHAT CAN YOU HEAR?

It's always noisy at the beach — with the waves crashing on the shore, seagulls screeching and squawking overhead, as well as people giggling and laughing. You might even hear the tinkle of the ice cream man arriving!

⭕ WHAT CAN YOU TASTE?

Yummy food is one of the most important parts of the beach! What kinds of treats will be in your poem — vanilla ice cream, big clouds of pink candyfloss, fish and chips eaten from newspapers out on the pier? Mmmm!

⭕ WHAT CAN YOU FEEL?

Maybe you feel warm, golden sand between your toes — or have you trodden on a squelchy piece of seaweed instead? Or perhaps you can feel your skin starting to get prickly because you forgot to put suntan lotion on? Oops!

DRAW YOUR OWN PRETTY GEM!

Get inspired by Emerald and Diamond and create and colour in your own gem in the space below!

Think about the shape of your gem. Will it be a heart, a classic round cut or a pretty pear shape?

What colour will your gem be? You could make it ruby red, swirly purple amethyst, brilliant yellow topaz or pretty rose quartz!

If you could give your gem to anyone, who would it be? Perhaps you could engrave their initials into it!

You could turn your gem into a ring, necklace, bracelet or earrings!

Maybe you'll be inspired by Jacky's jewellery and draw a moonstone set in fancy silver!

TURN TO PAGE 68 FOR MORE GEM INSPIRATION!

IMAGINE IF...

What would Hetty wear? Jeans and a t—shirt? A pretty dress like the ones she's always longed for? Maybe with her sewing skills she could design a brand—new style of dressing? Sketch a modern new outfit for Hetty here!

What kind of hobbies would Hetty have? Would she enjoy logging on to the internet or playing computer games? Perhaps she'd love playing outdoors on a scooter or bike. Write down some hobbies for Hetty!

....

....

....

....

What would modern—day Hetty be most surprised about? Would she be astonished to learn that there are no such things as foundlings any more? Is she amazed by technology like mobile phones? Is modern medicine the thing that she's most impressed with? Write down what you think Hetty would find amazing here!

....

....

....

....

....

WHY NOT?

Write a story about Hetty's first day in 2015 — what happens when she wakes up and finds herself in a new, futuristic world?

CREEPY CUSTOMS!

○ The Victorians loved the drama of death. They enjoyed reading spooky stories and gory tales of murder. When Prince Albert, Queen Victoria's beloved husband, died, she put on black mourning clothes and never wore colour again.

○ Soon everyone was copying the Queen and there were strict rules to follow after a loved one had died. Ladies were expected to mourn for at least two years!

FIRST MOURNING LASTED A YEAR AND A DAY. DRESSES WERE PLAIN, DULL BLACK AND MADE FROM A SPECIAL FABRIC CALLED CRAPE. THEY WERE WORN WITH A HEAVY BLACK BONNET AND VEIL. EVEN HANKIES AND UNDIES WERE TRIMMED WITH BLACK!

○ After first mourning, the clothes could have fancier trimmings and were made of finer materials like black silk.

I was going to fashion Mother a mourning bonnet to be proud of.

I worked on it all afternoon. I was not content with covering it in crape. I took the black silk mourning—band material and completely lined it, so it would be smooth against Mother's head. I took the black velvet and made soft new ribbons from it. It was now finely finished, but still very plain and sombre.

— Emerald Star

The only jewellery the Queen allowed at her royal court was made from jet, a fossilised wood from the sea. It could be carved into elaborate designs, but was still suitable for mourning because of the black colour.

DID YOU KNOW?
THE BEST JET JEWELLERY CAME FROM WHITBY, ONE OF JACKY'S FAVOURITE PLACES TO VISIT!

Jet soon became fashionable for all fine ladies, not just for those in mourning. It was expensive and people liked to show they could afford it. It was so stylish that cheaper copies made from glass and hard rubber soon began to appear.

Jewellery made from your loved one's hair was also popular. It was a way to keep a piece of them close after they'd gone and show how much they meant to you.

Instead of a knitting pattern in a magazine, you'd often find a braiding pattern for a bracelet, ring or earrings. Ladies would meet in the afternoons to chat and make hair jewellery.

DID YOU KNOW?
GIRLS WOULD ALSO MAKE BRAIDED HAIR FRIENDSHIP TOKENS TO SWAP WITH THEIR BESTIES!

LOCKS OF HAIR WERE STYLED INTO INTRICATE PATTERNS LIKE THIS AND HELD IN PLACE WITH FINE GOLD WIRES. LITTLE PEARLS REPRESENTED TEARS.

DID YOU KNOW?
QUEEN VICTORIA HAD A BRACELET BRAIDED FROM HER OWN HAIR AND GIFTED IT TO EMPRESS EUGENIE OF FRANCE.

A brooch or locket might spin round to show plain black to the outside and keep your loved one's hair next to your heart. Or sometimes a tiny picture or the name of the dead person was worked into the piece. Today this seems creepy, but it was all the rage in the 1800s!

Turn to page 73 to braid a bracelet for your BFF!

A Story of DRAMA & DESPAIR!

The Victorians loved tales of desperation and unfortunate events. Play this game to write your own heart—wrenching story of drama and despair!

Play as many times as you like!

PERSONALITY PICKER

Flip a coin to build a profile for your main character.

HEADS – boy
TAILS – girl

HEADS – kind
TAILS – spiteful

HEADS – honest
TAILS – cunning

HEADS – rich
TAILS – poor

HEADS – friendly
TAILS – lonely

HEADS – feisty
TAILS – meek

HEADS – funny
TAILS – sad

HEADS – lucky
TAILS – unlucky

Now write down a suitable name for your character —
play the Victorian name game on page 15 if you need some inspiration!

MAGIC NUMBERS

Use your own name to reveal your character's sad circumstance.

1 = ABC	4 = JKL	7 = STU
2 = DEF	5 = MNO	8 = VWX
3 = GHI	6 = PQR	9 = YZ

○ Add the numbers of your initials together, for example

HETTY FEATHER (H + F) IS 3 + 2 = 5

○ If your number is 10 or more, add the digits together until you get a number between 1 and 9, for example
10: 1 + 0 = 1

○ Now choose the story that matches your number

Use names of friends and family to create different unfortunate events!

1. Their family has died from influenza
2. Sent to work as a kitchen maid for a cruel master
3. Sells matches on the street for pennies
4. The family loses their wealth and becomes destitute
5. Is beaten and starved by their parents
6. Has been abandoned and left to survive alone
7. Is shunned by society because of a disability
8. Has lost their memory after an injury
9. Is forced to perform dangerous tricks for entertainment

BIRTHDAY MATCH

Use the month you were born to choose an interesting feature for your character.

JANUARY — Hair that's long enough to sit on

FEBRUARY — Two different coloured eyes

MARCH — Walks with a limp

APRIL — Never speaks

MAY — Has a spectacular singing voice

JUNE — Has a very noticeable birth mark

JULY — Is blind

AUGUST — Is an amazing actress

SEPTEMBER — Is an excellent thief

OCTOBER — Can't hear

NOVEMBER — Is incredibly beautiful

DECEMBER — Has six fingers on one hand

THINK CAREFULLY ABOUT HOW THE CIRCUMSTANCE AND FEATURE AFFECTS YOUR CHARACTER AND WORK IT INTO YOUR STORY. FOR EXAMPLE —

DO THEY USE THEIR ACTING TALENTS TO CON MONEY FROM PEOPLE? BUT THEN PERHAPS THEY NEED THE MONEY TO BUY MEDICINE FOR A SICK SIBLING...

PEOPLE WERE VERY MISTRUSTFUL OF THOSE WITH DISABILITIES, OFTEN SHUNNING THEM AND MAKING IT IMPOSSIBLE TO FIND WORK.

SELLING THEIR HAIR WAS A WAY FOR THE POOR TO MAKE MONEY.

WISHES & DREAMS

What keeps your character going through the toughest of times? Roll a dice to reveal a wish for them —

1. To live with a loving family

2. To become a famous artist

3. To find a cure for a dreadful illness

4. To become rich themselves and care for the less fortunate

5. To live as an writer in a little house by the sea

6. To marry their sweetheart and have their own children

Write down your results to get your story outline!

TURN TO PAGE 87 AND USE THE FORTUNE FINDER TO REVEAL A PLOT FOR YOUR DRAMATIC TALE!

CIRCUS QUIZ

Three times the fun!

Play with your friends!

Big Top True Or False!

1. Diamond performs with the Golden Tumblers.
2. Flora is a tightrope walker.
3. Elijah is the head lion.
4. Hetty fashions a ringmaster's costume for herself.
5. Little Diamond's doll is named Maybelle.
6. Chino the clown looks after the monkey family.

ANSWERS:
1. False — they are called the Silver Tumblers. 2. True. 3. False — Elijah is an elephant. 4. True. 5. True. 6. False — Mr Marvel takes care of the monkeys.

Class Clown or Star Student?

Pick three statements that sound most like you!

- ☐ I've never played a prank on my teacher
- ☐ I've laughed in class — a LOT!
- ☐ My jotter is covered in funny drawings and doodles.
- ☐ My homework is always in on time.
- ☐ I've never been late for class.
- ☐ I'm known for my hilarious impression of the strictest teacher in school.

Mostly Pink
You love learning and you even enjoy homework — well, some of the time! Find a good balance — there's plenty of time for study AND fun!

Mostly Purple
You often have your schoolmates in fits of giggles. Just remember to save your comedy routines for the playground, not the classroom!

CHALLENGE!

Can you separate the facts from the fibs?

T F
T F
T F
T F
T F
T F

Little Star!

Could you perform with Madame Adeline?

START

I CAN DO A HANDSTAND, EASY PEASY! — NO → **I'VE GOT GREAT BALANCE.** — NO → **SEQUINS AND SPARKLES ARE SO ME!**

I CAN DO A HANDSTAND — YES → **I'M TOTALLY FEARLESS.**

I'VE GOT GREAT BALANCE — YES → **I LOVE TO SHOW OFF!**

SEQUINS AND SPARKLES — YES → I LOVE TO SHOW OFF!

SEQUINS AND SPARKLES — NO → **I'M VERY ORGANISED.**

I'M TOTALLY FEARLESS — YES → **LITTLE STAR**

I'M TOTALLY FEARLESS — NO → I'M VERY ORGANISED

I LOVE TO SHOW OFF! — YES → I'M TOTALLY FEARLESS.

I LOVE TO SHOW OFF! — NO → I'M VERY ORGANISED.

I'M VERY ORGANISED — NO → LITTLE STAR

I'M VERY ORGANISED — YES → **LITTLE HELPER**

LITTLE STAR
You're a born performer! You'd love nothing more than to perform in a super–sparkly, show–stopping outfit in front of hundreds of adoring fans.

LITTLE HELPER
You really don't like to be in the spotlight! You'd much prefer to help out backstage, assisting the acts with their costume changes and learning their routines.

Will you be my star performer?

59

MARVELLOUS MEMOIRS

Hetty is skilled at making something out of nothing.
Make a beautiful Victorian journal from old things
— perfect for your memoirs!

YOU'LL NEED:

- Card — Hetty used old boxes
- Old paper or envelopes
- A used teabag
- Scraps of doily, paper, lace and ribbon
- Sticky foam pads
- Glue
- Cut—outs from pages 85 and 89
- Hole punch

1

Make a journal cover by cutting out two matching pieces of card. Hetty's journal measures 15cm square, but you can make yours any size you like. Place the two cover pieces together and punch holes on one edge like this

2

Spread out your scrap paper and cut open any envelopes. Give the paper an aged look by wiping it with the wet teabag and leave to dry.

4

Remake the holes by pushing a pencil down through them into a blob of sticky tack or clay.

3

Start to decorate your covers. Place on layers of paper or doilies and lace to create a lovely background. When you're happy with the design, stick everything in place.

TIP! Ask an adult to get some free wallpaper samples from a DIY store! Hetty's samples had patchwork and frame designs.

Stack your paper sheets together and cut some journal pages. Make them 1cm smaller than your cover — Hetty's are 14cm squared.
Line up your pages inside the cover and mark where the holes are with a pencil. Now punch through your stack of pages.

Add some Victorian cut—outs — make them 3D by sticking to card first then attaching to your cover with sticky pads. Use different thicknesses of pads to build up the effect.

Diamond is attached with one sticky pad layer.

Hetty is stuck flat to the background.

The frame is stuck on top with three layers of sticky pads.

The butterfly and the diamond are stuck on with two sticky pad layers.

To finish, put the journal pages inside the covers and thread pretty ribbon through the holes to hold it all together. Splendid!

Use things like bows, hearts, birds, fans and flowers to make a fabulous Victorian creation.

THE BIGGEST HETTY QUIZ EVER!

Read every book?
Test your Hetty Feather knowledge!

1 Can you match Hetty and Gideon to their Foundling numbers?

A. 25629   B. 25621
HETTY   GIDEON

2 Who does little Hetty push face-first into the pigsty?

....

3 What unusual animal does Hetty spot walking along a lane?

4 Who Said It?
"You are a child of Satan, Hetty Feather."

....

5 Who does Miss Smith treat to a meal of steak-and-kidney pudding?

Hetty and _____

6 Can you name this unscrupulous character?

....

7 Who steals Hetty's memoirs?
A. Mrs Briskett
B. Sarah   C. Mr Buchanan

8 Hetty offers to transcribe Mr Buchanan's writings in return for stamps.
☑ TRUE   ☐ FALSE

9 How tall does Mr Clarendon claim Fantastic Freda, the Female Giant is?
A. 6 feet
B. 7 feet
C. 10 feet!

10 Who Said It?
"You can be my little Hetty Hayseed."

....

EMERALD STAR (Jacqueline Wilson)

11 Can you remember what kind of fish Lizzie cooks for Hetty's breakfast?

14 Who Said It? "Oh, Hetty, it's the finest waistcoat I've ever seen."

12 Mina is Hetty's step–mother.

☐ TRUE   ☑ FALSE

15 Whose diary does Hetty sneak a peek at?

13 What kind of flowers does Hetty sew onto Mother's mourning hat?

DIAMOND (Jacqueline Wilson)

16 What is little Diamond's real name?

Ellen-Jane Potts

17 Who Said It? "You are my family now, Diamond. You and Madame Adeline."

18 Name the circus act!

19 Mr Marvel's baby monkey is called Maybelle.

TRUE ☑ OR FALSE? ☐

20 Hetty and Diamond make their escape on a ___ ___ ___ ___ ___ ___ — ___ ___ ___ ___ ___ ___ ___

How many did you get right?

ANSWERS:

HETTY FEATHER
1. Hetty – A, Gideon – B. 2. Saul.
3. Elephant. 4. Who Said It? Matron Bottomly.
5. Sissy.
SAPPHIRE BATTERSEA
6. Madame Berenice. 7. C. Mr Buchanan.
8. True. 9. B. 7 feet. 10. Bertie.
EMERALD STAR
11. Kippers. 12. False – Katherine is her step-mother. 13. Roses. 14. Jem. 15. Janet.
DIAMOND
16. Ellen-Jane Potts. 17. Hetty.
18. The Silver Tumblers. 19. False — it's Mavis. 20. Penny-farthing.

HETTY & ME

Hetty has a special place in my heart because...

HETTY FEATHER
Jacqueline Wilson
ILLUSTRATED BY NICK SHARRATT
Will Hetty ever find her true home?

1. She's so spirited and keeps fighting back no matter what.

2. She's loving and truly cares for her family and friends.

3. She's imaginative and makes up splendid stories and games.

4. She's daring and refuses to be intimidated.

5. She's great fun, so it's always a joy to write her story.

SAPPHIRE BATTERSEA
Jacqueline Wilson

EMERALD STAR
Jacqueline Wilson
ILLUSTRATED BY NICK SHARRATT

Who is YOUR favourite JW character and why? Jot down your five reasons here!

1. ....

2. ....

3. ....

4. ....

5. ....

DIAMOND

The spectacular tale of
Diamond, Acrobatic Child Wonder!
Starring friends old and new including the very special
guest, Hetty Feather! Diamond's heartbreaking story will have
you hooked — you'll laugh, you'll cry, you'll be amazed...

BORN: 1883
NAME: Ellen–Jane Potts
CIRCUS NAME: Diamond
performer of amazing acrobatic
twists and tumbles
LIKES: Her friend, Hetty Feather
DISLIKES: Beppo the clown

TURN OVER TO ENTER
DIAMOND'S WORLD OF THRILLS,
SPILLS, DARES AND DANGER...

INSIDE THE BIG TOP!

Roll up, roll up! Let's find out about the history of circuses!

MAGICAL MENAGERIES!

○ Circuses started out in ancient Egypt as collections of animals — called menageries — that travelled around so that people could see them.

○ In the 1800s, menageries became extremely popular — this was due to the fact that it was now easy to transport animals to different countries and, of course, everyone wanted to see the latest exotic animals for themselves!

○ As menageries toured local fairgrounds, soon the fun of the fair was paired with the allure of animals, and the circus was born!

○ In the 1830s, an American showman called Isaac Van Amburgh teamed up with a menagerie and became the world's first lion—tamer. His trick of putting his head in a lion's mouth apparently impressed Queen Victoria when she saw it!

COLOURFUL CLOWNS!

○ Clowns became popular at circuses after a performer called Joseph Grimaldi used traditional pantomime characters to create a humorous performance. He is credited with creating the white—faced clown make—up we recognise today!

○ There are different types of clowns that have different personalities. A Pierrot is a sad, downbeat character who is often the butt of jokes and usually appears with a painted tear on his face. Harlequin, on the other hand, is a light—hearted, mischievous character who often takes part in slapstick comedy, and is recognisable from his chequered outfit.

SUPER STRONGMEN!

○ Strongmen often appeared at circuses, displaying feats of strength like balancing weights on their heads, or lifting incredible heavy objects.

○ One of the most famous strongmen, Joseph Greenstein, was known as the Mighty Atom and was reported to be able to bite nails in half with his teeth!

TERRIFIC TRICK RIDERS!

○ One of the earliest acts to appear in circuses was trick riding, which involved skilled acrobats riding horses round the ring, performing tricks on the horses' backs.

○ A man called Philip Astley is thought to have been the first trick rider, starting his act in the 1700s. His wife, Patty, also became a trick rider, and one of her more daring stunts was to ride around with bees covering her hands and arms — what a feat!

Can you think of a trick rider in the Hetty Feather books?

TANGLEFIELD'S CIRCUS

WHAT'S YOUR CIRCUS SKILL?

Tick the boxes to find out what your circus talent is!

☐ I LIKE MAKING PEOPLE LAUGH!
☐ I'M VERY DARING!
☐ I LOVE ANIMALS!
☐ I'M ALWAYS TELLING JOKES!
☐ I DO GYMNASTICS OR DANCING!
☐ I KEEP MY COOL UNDER PRESSURE!
☐ I'M GOOD AT BALANCING ON ONE LEG!
☐ I CAN JUGGLE!
☐ I NEVER GET SCARED!

MOSTLY PINK!
You're a natural entertainer because you love to make people laugh and smile... and that's why you'd make an excellent clown! Throw a bit of juggling or slapstick into the mix and you'll have the audience chortling like never before!

MOSTLY BLUE!
You're fabulously fearless and let nothing scare you — that's why you'd be a brilliant lion tamer! You're calm and collected, and you'd let those big, scary lions know who's boss. The audience would ooh and ahh at your bravery!

MOSTLY PURPLE!
You're great at gymnastics and love animals, so you'd be a terrific trick rider, just like Madame Adeline! High on the back of a magnificent steed, you'd gracefully twist and tumble and delight the audience with your every move!

67

DESIGN WITH DIAMOND!

Bring Diamond's world to life with a splash of colour and creativity!

TANGLEFIE

68

BIG TOP POM-POMS

Make show—stopping decorations from old t—shirts!

1.

Draw two circles on the cardboard, each approximately 14cm wide — we drew round a bowl . Draw a smaller circle within each circle — these should be around 6cm wide. Carefully cut them out.

2.

Cut a small wedge from your cardboard templates to create a gap.

Take one strip and sandwich it between the two templates. We used the hem of the t—shirt because it's thicker and stronger.

4.

Place the other ring on top!

3.

Lay out your t—shirt and cut strips of around 1½cm thick.

YOU'LL NEED:

★ An old t-shirt

★ Cardboard

(one t-shirt makes one pom-pom)

★ Scissors

TIP!
Take your scissors and trim your pom-pom to give it a nice, round fluffy shape!

Start to wind your strips round the template, pulling them tightly as you go.

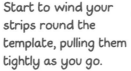

5.

6.

When you reach the end of a strip, secure it by wrapping the next strip over the top.

7.

Keep winding until you have three layers. Carefully take the ends of the sandwiched strip and loosely knot them together to hold your layers in place while you cut.

8.

Very carefully, snip the fabric layers along the side of the template. Use your other hand to hold the strips in place. Gently remove the cardboard templates and pull the sandwiched strings as tight as they will go. Tie in a secure knot to hold your pom-pom together.

★ THE BIG TOP TEST!

Quiz yourself with these circus words!

After reading *Diamond*, you'll be familiar with circus words such as Big Top (a large tent where the circus is performed) and Ringmaster (the person who announces the circus acts), but do you know what the words below mean?

TANGLEFIELD'S CIRCUS

1. TURNAWAY
A) Someone who is turned away because they're not dressed appropriately
B) A sold-out show
C) A circus act performed outside the Big Top

2. VENDOR
A) Someone who sells snacks and souvenirs
B) A special guest in the audience
C) A worker who builds the Big Top

3. ROUSTABOUT
A) Benches that circus performers sit on
B) The whip that a lion tamer uses
C) A circus workman

4. FUNAMBULIST
A) A member of the audience who's disruptive
B) A tightrope walker
C) A grumpy backstage worker

5. CALLIOPE
A) A troop of galloping horses
B) A musical instrument much like an organ
C) The smallest circus performer

6. TRUNK UP
A) A clown's dress rehearsal
B) A performer who dives into a small pool
C) A command to elephants to raise their trunks in salute

★ FAB PHRASES!

These well-known phrases originated in the circus. Try using them in your own story!

HOLD YOUR HORSES
Then: Horse handlers said this to calm down their animals.
Now: Be patient.

GET THIS SHOW ON THE ROAD
Then: Let's go!
Now: Let's go!

RAIN OR SHINE
Then: The circus will still perform regardless of the weather.
Now: Nothing will stand in my way!

Answers:
1) B 2) A 3) C 4) B 5) B 6) C

PRETTY BRAIDED BRACELET

With a little practice you can make...

...a Victorian knotted friendship token for your bestie.

1. You'll need three pieces of string or wool braided together, or a thick piece of string. Place the braid flat on the table. Cross the right over the left and under as if you were beginning to tie a knot.

2. Turn your half-knot upside down like this

You should have a longer tail on the right—hand side.

3. Take the right—hand tail and loop it back towards the knot. Tuck it under the middle strand

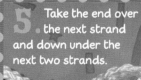

4. Now loop the end back round towards the right and under the first strand you come to. Bring the end through to the top like this

Why Not?

- Start with a longer braid and make a necklace.
- Glue a knotted heart to a card for a loved one.

5. Take the end over the next strand and down under the next two strands.

Then bring it up to the top again through the space between the last two strands like this

6. To finish, very gently tighten the knot. Carefully pull one side a little, then the other. Flatten and shape into a heart by easing the string round in the centre of the knot before pulling tighter again.

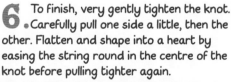

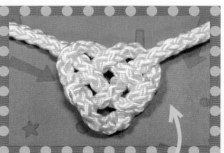

Don't rush — it's easy to get into a tangle at this point! If you get stuck just remember the ends of the braid will be at the top of the finished heart.

73

FRIENDS FOREVER!

Hetty and Diamond's guide to being a fabulous friend!

Stick Up For Them!

HETTY: When your friend feels like she's been treated unfairly, you should support her as much as you can. When Matron Peters swished my friend Janet for getting her bs and ds the wrong way round, I told Matron Peters it was unfair. Friends always stick up for each other!

Be Confident!

DIAMOND: If your friend's feeling down, help her see the good in the situation. It's always much easier to see the wonderful things in other people than it is to see them in yourself and it'll give your friend a happy boost. Hetty made me feel so much better about my new name. She said it didn't matter a jot if you change your name — she'd changed hers three times!

HETTY AND DIAMOND ARE BFS, BUT HOW MANY OTHER JW BEST FRIENDS CAN YOU NAME?

Appreciate Them!

HETTY: Tell your friends how much they mean to you. Write them a special letter or arrange a fun get—together. I was so happy to have made two friends at the terrible Foundling Hospital, Harriet and Nurse Winterson. I appreciated them all the more when I was utterly friend—less at night.

WHY NOT?
MAKE A CARD FOR YOUR FRIEND AND WRITE DOWN THREE THINGS YOU LOVE ABOUT HER!

Help Out!

DIAMOND: If your friend wants to be better at something, why not help her out? She might be terrible at maths when you're great, so you could give her a hand with her homework. Or how about lending her your art set when she wants to draw a beautiful picture? Hetty tried to teach me how to read and even read me her favourite book, *David Copperfield*. It made me feel hopeful.

STORIES FOR GIRLS

Have Fun!

DIAMOND: Enjoy spending time together and laugh a lot. Hetty and I ran wild races and stole the clowns' penny—farthing, but we had wonderful quiet times together too. These are the times you'll look back on fondly and giggle about in future!

DIAMOND'S CONFIDENCE CHALLENGE!

How to be more confident in five steps!

1. Stand up straight — if you look confident, you'll feel more confident! I couldn't be an Amazing Acrobat if I didn't have the posture to go with it!

2. Wear a smile! Everyone will think you look approachable and friendly!

3. Write down all the things you're good at, or get a friend to write a list for you. It'll give you a real boost.

4. When someone says something nice about you, say thank you instead of shrugging it off. Remember the lovely comments and ignore the nasty remarks!

5. Remember that most people feel insecure at times. Even at Tanglefield's we'd get nervous before our performance but it was worth it for the standing ovation at the end!

STAR OF THE SHOW?

Find your big top destiny!

START

It's school play time. You volunteer for

THE STARRING ROLE! → You dream of being an actress.

SOMETHING BACKSTAGE. → Friends describe you as...

LOUD

QUIET → You love being asked to read out loud in class!

NO

YES → You get embarrassed...

NEVER! → You've been accused of being a show-off!

EASILY!

YES

NO → Which character is most like you?

HETTY

DIAMOND → The thought of standing on stage in front of an audience fills you with...

YES → You'd rather sing...

NO

ON *THE X FACTOR*!

EXCITEMENT!

IN THE SHOWER!

DREAD!

YOU'RE BIG TOP BOLD!

Nothing thrills you more than the thought of being centre—stage, in front of a massive audience, performing your socks off! You're destined to be in the limelight, just like Mistress of the ring, Emerald Star!

YOU'RE SPOTLIGHT SHY!

The thought of having to stand up in front of people and perform terrifies you — that's why you'd much prefer a behind—the—scenes role! You'd be great at taking care of all the costumes or performing in a disguise like Beppo the clown.

HOW TO DRAW:
TANGLEFIELD'S BIG TOP!

Nick shows you how!

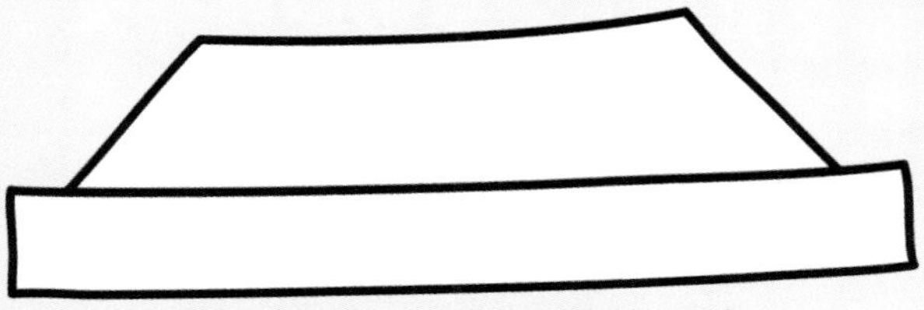

1 Draw a long rectangle — this will be the big top sign. Then draw three straight lines to make the tent roof.

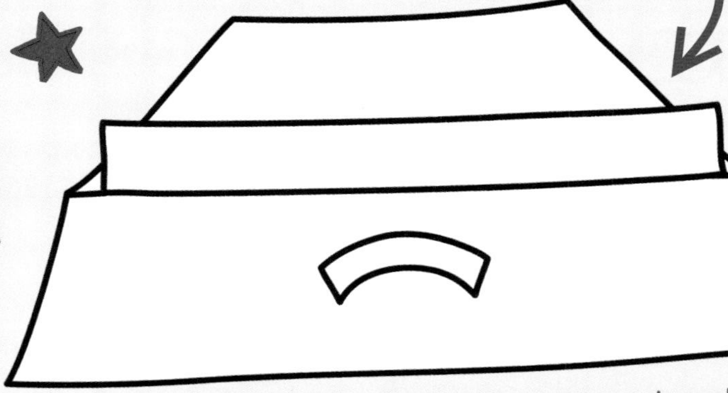

2 Now sketch a slightly longer line underneath the big top sign. Draw two slightly curved lines towards the ground, then join them up with another straight line. Add a couple of lines to join up where the roof and the wall meet. Don't forget to add the semi-circle panel above the doorway!

3 Next, add the doorway and shade it in black. Add two small triangles at the top for flags.

NICK'S TIP!

Why not try using some different colours for the tent? Or a different pattern on the fabric?

4

TANGLEFIELD'S CIRCUS

Finally, write Tanglefield's Circus on the sign, then colour in the big top with bright stripes!

WOULD YOU BE

Uh-oh — you've been sold to the circus for five guineas, just like Diamond. But what happens next?

SCENE 1:

YOU'VE JUST ARRIVED AT THE CIRCUS AND ARE STRUGGLING WITH YOUR SUITCASE.

HEADS

The resident Strong Man just so happens to be walking past and kindly picks up your luggage with just his pinky finger. Wow!

TAILS

You have to leave it behind when you can't carry it any longer. You have to wear the clown's spare clothes now — including his GIANT shoes!

SCENE 2:

YOU'RE SHOWN TO WHERE YOU'LL BE STAYING. WHAT IS IT LIKE?

HEADS

You've got your very own wooden trailer! It's painted red and gold and inside it's cosy and warm — you even have a little fireplace!

TAILS

You're bunking down in a TINY trailer with six trapeze artists, two clowns and a fortune teller. Oh yes, and a sea lion. It's pretty crowded!

SCENE 3:

THE WHOLE CIRCUS GOES ON PARADE THROUGH THE LOCAL TOWN. YOU...

HEADS

Sit in a gilt carriage pulled by prancing white horses dressed up with pink feathers, and charm the crowds with your big smile!

TAILS

Get thrown off your horse and into a muddy puddle. The entire crowd points and laughs and you're completely humiliated. And wet.

SCENE 6:

THE CLOWNS ROPE YOU INTO THEIR PERFORMANCE.

HEADS

You have a merry old time 'accidentally' throwing custard pies at people in the audience. It's all part of the act, of course!

TAILS

Um, did you not mention your total fear of clowns?! You scream in fright before running away and hiding under an elephant.

SCENE 7:

YOU'RE ON IN FIVE MINUTES, BUT YOU DROP YOUR COSTUME IN A PUDDLE!

HEADS

You enlist the friendly circus fire breather to dry it off for you — at a safe distance, naturally.

TAILS

You have to perform in your soaking wet costume and are a snivelling, shivering bed-ridden mess for the rest of the week.

SCENE 8:

SOMEONE FALLS ILL AND YOU HAVE TO HELP OUT. WHO IS IT?

HEADS

The ticket seller. You sit in the ticket booth for a couple of hours and then you get to watch the whole show — in the best seats in the house!

TAILS

The human cannonball. You've been given a silver helmet and a new nickname — The Bullet — but you have a feeling this is going to hurt...

A CIRCUS STAR?

How To Play:

Flip a coin to see which outcome you get!

SCENE 4:

YOU'RE ASKED TO HELP TO WASH THE ELEPHANT.

HEADS

Elijah loves the pedicure you give him so much that he picks you up with his trunk and takes you on a tour of the circus!

TAILS

Elijah takes a dislike to you and stamps on your foot — ouch! You're then left to pick up his toenail cuttings from the ground — eww!

SCENE 5:

YOU'RE PUT IN A COSTUME AND TOLD TO WALK THE TRAPEZE.

HEADS

You discover you have a natural talent for acrobatics and wow the audience with your tricks!

TAILS

You fall off a couple of steps in and land in a heap in the lion's cage. And he's looking kind of hungry too...

SCENE 9:

THE RINGMASTER CALLS YOU TO HIS TENT. WHAT DOES HE WANT?

HEADS

He wants to congratulate you on your recent performances and inform you that he's giving you a pay rise. Hooray!

TAILS

He tells you that you're useless as a circus performer and your new role is to muck out all the animals. Mmmm... stinky.

SCENE 10:

IT'S A YEAR SINCE YOU WERE SOLD TO THE CIRCUS FOR A PENNY.

HEADS

You're now worth thousands of pounds and perform at shows all over the country as the headline act!

TAILS

You're still cleaning out the animals. And even they don't like you very much — Elijah squirted you with water last week. Huff!

Use the outcomes you've chosen to write a story about what happens next!

WRITE YOUR STORY HERE:

79

TASTY CIRCUS SNACKS!

Roll up, roll up and enjoy these circus snacks!

DIAMOND'S DELICIOUS BISCUITS

Makes 16 biscuits!

Amazing cookies to share with your loved ones!

You'll need:

- 150g plain flour
- 100g margarine or butter
- 50g caster sugar
- Sprinkles
- Gold or silver edible balls

1. Pre-heat oven to 180°C (350°F/Gas Mark 4) and lightly grease baking trays.

2. Sift flour into a mixing bowl and stir in the sugar. Rub in the margarine with your hands to create a soft dough. Bring the dough together in a ball then roll out on a flat surface till ½cm thick.

The dough will take around 3–5 minutes to form.

3. Use a star shaped cutter to cut out the cookies. Place on a baking tray and bake in the oven for 15 minutes or till golden brown. Leave to cool for 5 minutes then transfer to a wire rack to cool completely. Your cookies should look like this!

4. Follow the icing recipe opposite and use pink and yellow food colouring to dye it. Dip the biscuits in the icing and add sprinkles and edible balls to decorate. Leave to set for 15 minutes — then enjoy!

BITE-SIZE BEPPOS!

Make these sweet treats for your next sleepover!

You'll need:

- White marshmallows
- Blue or green writing icing pen
- Sprinkles
- Round red sweets

1. Use the cut-out-and-keep icing recipe below to make plain white icing. Spread the icing on the top of a marshmallow then dip in a bowl of sprinkles. This will create Beppo's cool clown hair!

2. For Beppo's big red nose, spread some icing on a red sweet then stick it in the middle of the marshmallow like this

3. Finally, use a writing icing pen to pipe two small eyes above his nose. So cute!

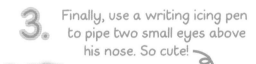

Cut out and keep!

WATER ICING RECIPE

Ingredients:

- 100g icing sugar
- 2 tbsp water
- Food colouring (optional)

○ Place the icing sugar in a bowl and gradually stir in the water until you make a paste. This is a basic white icing — it should coat the back of a spoon but not be too thick to spread.

○ To make a colourful icing, just add a few drops of food colouring until you get the colour you like.

Ask an adult to help you in the kitchen!

Enough to ice up to 24 biscuits, a medium cake or 12 cupcakes!

VICTORIAN VIPS!

These Victorians were the celebrities of their time!

FAMOUS VICTORIANS!

ALEXANDER GRAHAM BELL is famous for inventing the telephone! Lots of other inventors were working on the idea at the time, but he was the first one to succeed in 1876. He beat another inventor by a mere two hours!

★ ★ ★

LEWIS CARROLL is the author of *Alice In Wonderland*, which was published in 1865. He used to take his friend's daughters out for boat trips on the river and tell them stories. One of these stories turned into the book!

Yum!

JOHN CADBURY was the person who brought us Cadbury's chocolate! His first shop actually sold silk and drapery, but luckily for us he opened his first chocolate factory in 1831. In 1854 John and his brother were given the Royal Warrant — it meant they were the official chocolate and cocoa maker for Queen Victoria!

FLORENCE NIGHTINGALE was something of a celebrity during this era. Her wealthy parents didn't approve of her choice of career because at the time, nurses came from poor families. However, she stuck to her guns and changed the way hospitals were run for the better!

★ ★ ★

 LORD SHAFTESBURY was a politician who tried to improve children's lives during the Victorian era. In 1833 he proposed that children should work for a maximum of ten hours a day — that's less than they were currently working at the time. He also banned children under nine from working in textile factories. What a nice man!

VICTORIAN INVENTIONS!

- **THE PHOTOGRAPH.** Victorian people would get dressed up in their best clothes but it would take at least TEN MINUTES for one photo to be taken! Zzzzz...

- **THE PENNY BLACK STAMP** was the first ever stick—on postage stamp. It featured Queen Victoria's profile against a black background, and cost one penny.

- **THE FIRST CARS** appeared during the Victorian era. Only rich people could afford them though, and early drivers had to have an attendant walking in front of the car waving a red warning flag!

- This one is our favourite! In 1864 the first ever **JELLY BABIES** were invented by Herr Steinbeck. Nom nom nom!

WHAT WOULD YOU INVENT?

1. **YOU'VE GOT A TEST IN SCIENCE CLASS TOMORROW. YOU**
A) Can't wait to show off how clever you are!
B) Are in a mild state of panic. You hate science!

2. **IF YOU COULD BE SOMEONE ELSE FOR A DAY, YOU'D BE...**
A) Einstein. Yes, you're a geek. But what a brain!
B) Willy Wonka. Maybe he could give you a job!

3. **IN YOUR GROUP OF FRIENDS YOU ARE...**
A) The logical one. You never lose your temper!
B) The kind and generous one! You're a sweetheart.

4. **AT LUNCHTIME YOU'RE MOST LIKELY TO BE MUNCHING ON...**
A) Lots of fruit. All those vitamins are good for your brain!
B) Um... sweeties. You do share them though!

5. **IT'S SATURDAY AFTERNOON. WHAT ARE YOU DOING?**
A) Watching a sci—fi movie or reading.
B) Making cake pops for a sleepover that night.

MOSTLY As

You'd invent something scientific! It might be a cure for a disease or a nifty new gadget that would help to make people's lives a little easier — but if anyone's going to do it, it's you! You're a bit of a boffin!

MOSTLY Bs

You'd invent a new treat! Cadbury's chocolate and jelly babies came out of the Victorian era, but you think you could dream up something even better! And you'd have lots of fun sampling your efforts too!

EMERALD EVER AFTER!

You can write the next chapter of Emerald and Diamond's story!

Hover your hand over the page, then say the following:

EMERALD AND DIAMOND, BEST OF FRIENDS, I WANT TO KNOW WHAT HAPPENS NEXT!

Then close your eyes, circle your hand three times and bring it down on to the page. The plotline your index finger lands on is the one you should continue!

EMERALD AND DIAMOND RUN OFF TO START THEIR OWN CIRCUS, WHICH FAST BECOMES KNOWN AS THE GREATEST IN THE LAND!

TANGLEFIELD'S CIRCUS

THEIR MEMOIRS ARE READ BY A FAMOUS AUTHOR WHO DEMANDS THAT THEY BE PUBLISHED — EMERALD AND DIAMOND: AUTHORS EXTRAORDINAIRE!

AFTER LIVING A LIFE WITH NO REAL FAMILY OF THEIR OWN, THE GIRLS DECIDE TO OPEN A HOME FOR ORPHANED AND ABANDONED CHILDREN.

EMERALD IS REUNITED WITH EITHER BERTIE OR JEM (YOU CHOOSE WHO!) AND ASKS DIAMOND TO BE HER BRIDESMAID AT THEIR WEDDING!

WITH EMERALD'S HELP, DIAMOND GOES BACK TO FIND HER SIBLINGS. WILL THEY EVER MEET AGAIN?

THE GIRLS DECIDE TO RETIRE FROM CIRCUS LIFE AND MOVE INTO A LITTLE COTTAGE BESIDE THE SEA TOGETHER.

THEY GO TO STAY WITH MADAME ADELINE — BUT WILL IT BE HAPPILY EVER AFTER?

What do you think will happen next? Write down your story outline here...

CUT-OUT CURIOSITIES

Cut and stick embellishments for your fabulous Victorian creations.

Personalise your possessions! Stick letters to your journals and books.

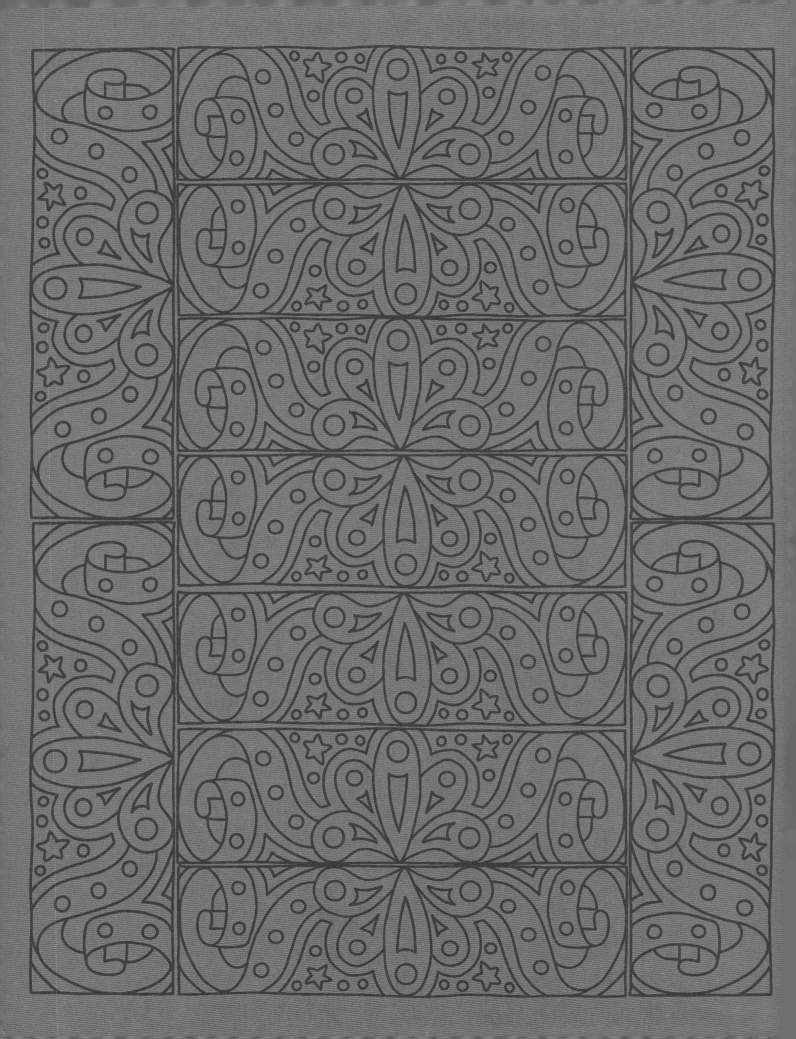

WHAT'S THE PLOT?

Use this to pick a plot for your story of drama and despair from page 56.

despair from page 56.

HOW TO PLAY:
○ Pick a number between 1 and 4.
○ Open and close the square the same number of times.
○ Pick a character.
○ Open and close again as you spell out their name.
○ Pick another character and look under the flap to find your story setting.

MAKE IT!

1. Cut out the square and turn it over so this side is face down.

2. Fold each corner into the centre to make a smaller square.

3. Turn it back over, fold the corners into the centre again then fold the square in half.

4. Put a thumb and index finger under each numbered flap and push the four corners together to meet in the middle.

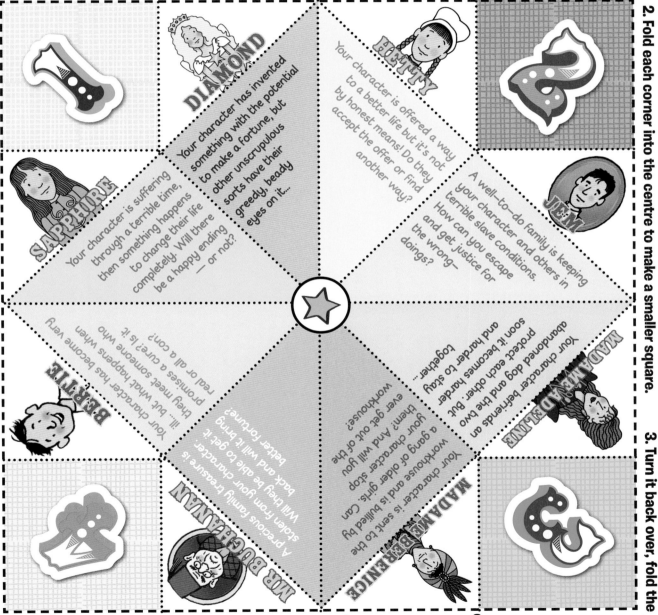

DIAMOND

Your character has invented something with the potential to make a fortune, but other unscrupulous sorts have their greedy, beady eyes on it...

POLLY

Your character is offered a way to a better life but it's not by honest means! Do they accept the offer or find another way?

JEM

A well-to-do family is keeping your character and others in terrible slave conditions. How can you escape and get justice for the wrong-doings?

MADAM ADELINE

Your character befriends an abandoned dog and the two protect each other, but soon it becomes harder and harder to stay together...

MADAME BERENICE

Your character is sent to the workhouse and is bullied by a gang of older girls. Can your character stop them? And will you ever get out of the workhouse?

MR BUCKMANN

A precious family treasure is stolen from your character. Will they be able to get it back and will it bring better fortune?

BERTIE

Your character has become very ill... but what happens when they meet someone who promises a cure? Is it real or all a con?

SAPPHIRE

Your character is suffering through a terrible time, then something happens to change their life completely. Will there be a happy ending — or not?

Now you've created a character and picked a story plot, so get writing! Try to work in all your results for a tale of drama and despair!

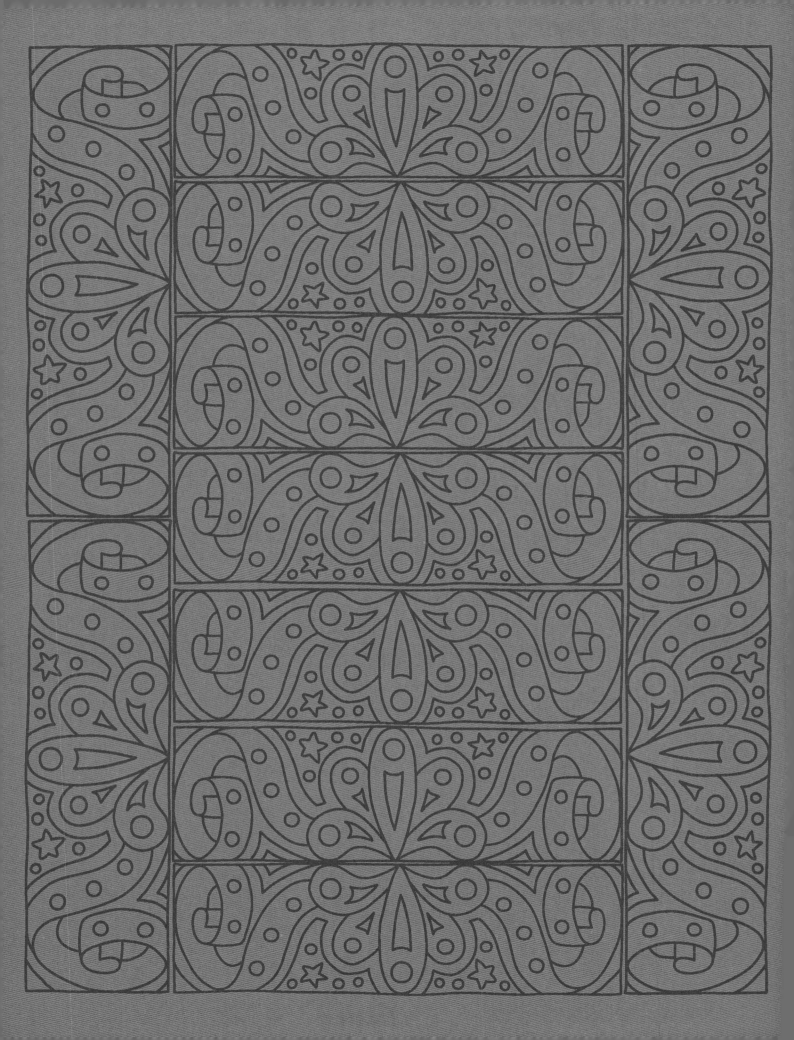

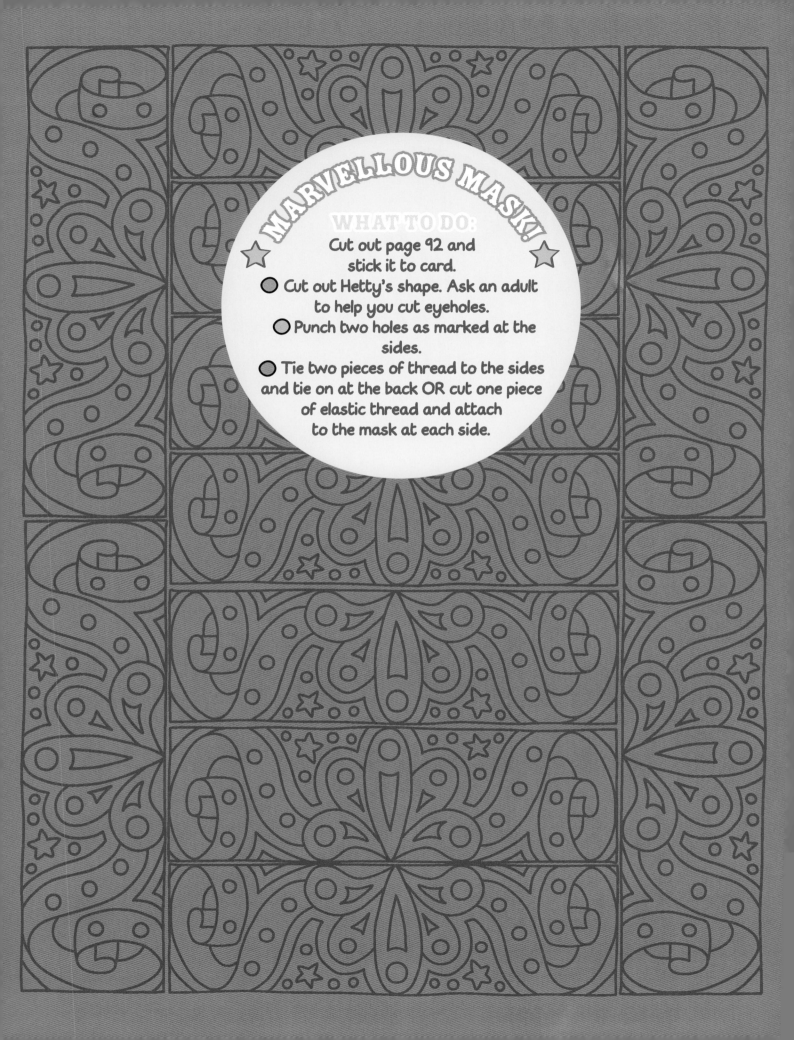

MARVELLOUS MASK!

WHAT TO DO:

Cut out page 92 and
stick it to card.

● Cut out Hetty's shape. Ask an adult
to help you cut eyeholes.

○ Punch two holes as marked at the
sides.

○ Tie two pieces of thread to the sides
and tie on at the back OR cut one piece
of elastic thread and attach
to the mask at each side.

The Official Jacqueline Wilson Mag

16 issues for the price of 10*

SAVE £23 ON THE SHOP PRICE!*

FULL OF BRILLIANT FEATURES!

- ☑ Exclusive writing tips from Jacqueline Wilson
- ☑ Draw with Nick Sharratt
- ☑ Fun puzzles
- ☑ A letter from Jacqueline Wilson in every issue
- ☑ Amazing presents with every issue!
- ☑ Learn all about Jacky's brilliant books

HOW TO GET THIS OFFER

Ask an adult to...

⭐ Visit www.jw-mag.com/subscriptions

⭐ Call free on 0800 318 846
(8am–9pm, 7 days. Freephone from UK landlines only)

⭐ Please quote JWANN when ordering